# The ADDICTOHOLIC DECONSTRUCTED

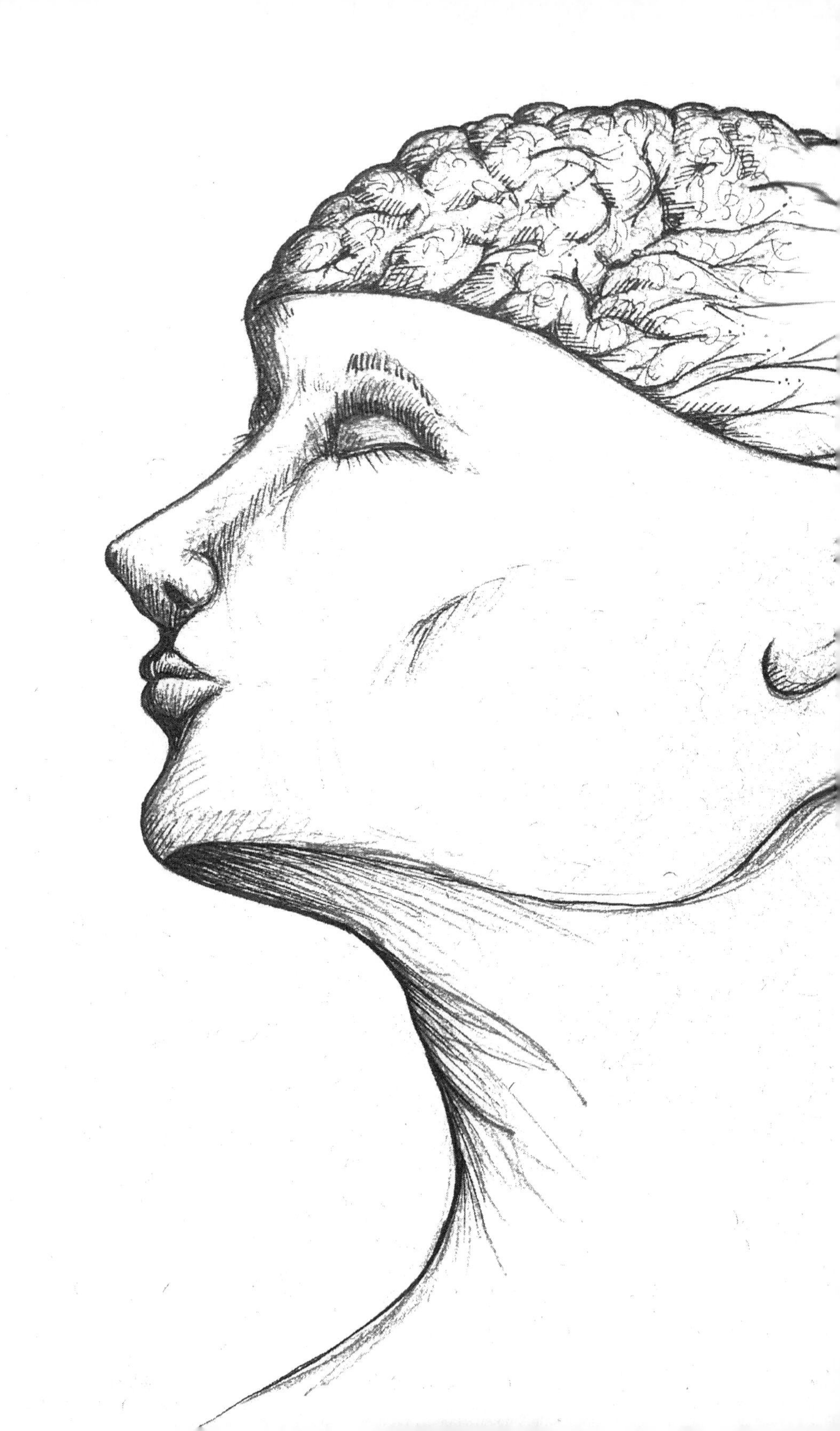

# The Addictoholic Deconstructed

An irreverently quick and dirty
education by a doctor who says f*ck, a lot.

Dr. Nicole Labor, DO

Although the author and publisher have made every effort to ensure that the information in this book was correct at press time, the author and publisher do not assume and hereby disclaim any liability to any party for any loss, damage, or disruption caused by errors or omissions, whether such errors or omissions result from negligence, accident, or any other cause.

Adherence to all applicable laws and regulations, including international, federal, state and local governing professional licensing, business practices, advertising, and all other aspects of doing business in the US, Canada or any other jurisdiction is the sole responsibility of the reader and consumer.

Neither the author nor the publisher assumes any responsibility or liability whatsoever on behalf of the consumer or reader of this material. Any perceived slight of any individual or organization is purely unintentional. The resources in this book are provided for informational purposes only and should not be used to replace the specialized training and professional judgment of a health care or mental health care professional.

Neither the author nor the publisher can be held responsible for the use of the information provided within this book. Please always consult a trained professional before making any decision regarding treatment of yourself or others.

This book is dedicated to my parents,
who taught me about unconditional love and support.

To my husband, Lee,
who has taught me about the true give and take of love.

To my daughter, Verity,
who has taught me what it is to be love.

In loving memory of:
Theresa LaRocco Graham
Isabella LaRocco
Garry M. Ballerini

## TABLE OF CONTENTS

*“The beginning is the most important part of the work.”*

-Plato

# FOREWARD:

Emotional healing is about telling stories. We do this so that we remind ourselves and others that there is a beginning, middle and end to a disease process, and this helps create hope, generate determination and empathy. For years, as I have described my work to those who don't know much about it, I have said that I get to hear the best stories in the world. Best in terms of being sometimes unbelievable (active addiction) and sometimes moving (recovery). Dr. Labor's story is one that fits both descriptions. I have been privileged to know her during all phases of illness and wellness, and I am most gratified to be her colleague, after being the doctor and the teacher. I am looking forward to working with her in the realm of the meta state of addiction medicine, after working with her on her personal recovery and then seeing her establish herself as a professional.

That meta state of addiction medicine is in an active part of its' story. As of this moment, September, 2019, the field is in flux and change, with all the triumph and distress that change can bring. I expect and hope that this change will be for the good, in the long run, making it possible to better address the brain disease that we call addiction. Along the way, there is tumult.

When I began my career in the early 90's, cocaine was the drug of the moment. We had limited tools to treat it; neither the pharmaceutical industry or any other large, established organization had much interest in it. Payment for treatment was poor, both from commercial payers and federal benefits, and the groups who were providing treatment did so largely out of dedication to a cause. Most of the folks who did this, doctors, nurses, counselors were all in recovery themselves and the overwhelming majority of those folks got into recovery through working in 12-step programs. While there was a small group of patients who had opiate dependence (as we called it back then) and were on methadone, this treatment was stigmatized by those in other forms of recovery, as well as the medical community and the lay public, and was not uniformly available. At that time, much of what was known and done about addiction treatment came through the lens of 12-step work.

12-step work, in addition to the fascinating science of the brain, is what drew me to the field. I am lucky enough that I have not needed to go to meetings to create a manageable life, but I have gained wisdom from the meetings I have attended. There is an incredible, loving, warm humanity that you see in 12-step work. I have heard it likened to the cartoons one sees in the New Yorker, where you end up laughing at the cartoon because you've been in that same spot so many times. Early on in my work, several people asked what it would be like if there ever were a pill that could be taken to "cure" addiction, and I would reply that it would be a loss. I still see 12-step work, like the work that gets done in good psychotherapy, to be remarkable, transformative and probably the most important thing that people can do with their lives. Now, however, I am seeing a significant value to that pill.

Dr. Labor makes the point that getting to abstinence and recovery is HARD work. It takes great courage to look at oneself and see all the warts and foibles. It takes persistence, determination and a great support group to persist in the work, which is never ending. You can't help but admire someone who has been doing this, and there is no difference if the recovery is from a traumatic injury, cancer, a birth abnormality or addictive disease. We respect anyone who is courageous, strong, humble, because they are great people. Those qualities describe the folks we allwant to spend time with.

Much of what the recent opiate crisis has brought to light is that not everyone who has the disease will be able to do that hard work. Not everyone who has lost a limb is going to compete in the para-Olympics. Not everyone who has cancer is going to be able to tolerate the therapies necessary to treat the cancer. That doesn't mean that those lives have no meaning, or that the people described don't deserve respect and love. This is the stance that we have taken with addiction for decades. In part because we have not had universally effective and accessible treatment, we've glibly dismissed those who couldn't do all that very hard work as being "constitutionally incapable," and we've blamed the victim. I have been part of this, and I wish that I had done differently. People have been shunned, disparaged, thrown out of treatment because they were constitutionally incapable. I don't think that we yet have the capability or the capacity to treat all the people who were labelled this way, but I hope that we are moving in that direction. The fact that those groups that have the resources to influence governments and large organizations have largely used alcohol and prescription pharmaceuticals meant that it was easier to disparage those marginalized groups who used illicit or illegal substances.

There has evolved a tension between groups who subscribe to different kinds of treatment methods. In the broadest sense, this is nonsensical, but, that's what humans do. So, there are those who see 12-step work as the only way to achieve "real" recovery, and those who see everyone who has an addiction as being also diagnosed with a psychiatric disorder, and those who see medications as being a who answer. Seeing these tensions play out between colleagues and patients is sad. There are people who are not getting treatment that would help them because of this tension and there are people who are retreating from others they used to be friendly with because of it. I recognize this as part and parcel of change, but it is sad.

Another aspect of the change that has become apparent is that there is now money to be made in treating addiction, and most specifically, opiate addiction. This has had life-enhancing effects, and some really nasty effects. Pharmaceutical and software companies, healthcare systems have now begun creating and offering treatment, where they weren't interested in doing so several decades ago. This is leading to new medications, creative and innovative treatments, but also situations that are labelled as treatment which are not effective and are being offered aggressively and billed for, generating fraud claims, uncertainty and ill will. Federal, state and local governments are now trying to be helpful, though the result is sometimes money flowing without much direction, which is wasteful at best.

An aspect of this change story that is near and dear to my heart has to do with the recognition of addiction medicine as a subspecialty. At the beginning of my career, one of my mentors, Sid Schnoll, MD, PhD, invited me to work with him on the committee that prepared the certification examination for the American Society of Addiction Medicine. The exam was recognized at the time by those few health systems and insurers who dealt with this as being a marker of expertise. I remember distinctly that Sid did not see that this would ever become an exam that was administered through the American Board of Medical Specialties (this group is the ultimate decider about what is a medical specialty), that the path to achieving this was too complicated by stigma and the desire of all involved that physicians from all primary specialties be eligible. (Remember, many of the doctors who want to treat people with addiction are in recovery, themselves – and they often got into recovery long after starting their careers in internal medicine, family practice, obstetrics, etc. We want the exam to be available to all.) I started working on the exam in about 2000. In the last 19 years, I have seen first, the establishment of an independent board (the American Board of Addiction Medicine) and then the assumption of the examination by a committee under the American Board of Preventive Medicine (Preventive Medicine is part of the American Board of Medical Specialties). This means that the diagnosis, treatment and prevention of addiction disease is treated the same way as heart disease or cancer, in terms of organized medicine. This also means that there is accountability, recognition, some money flowing into training.

All of this has meant that those of us who have been involved for a very long time are seeing things happen that we never expected: money for training, calls to come testify to Congress, lots of job opportunities, lots of people wanting our expert opinions. But there's more work to be done than anyone can handle to treat all the patients who can now afford treatment, to train the new doctors, to help write the policies. It is beyond our wildest dreams and our hair is on fire. As my dear friend Dave Withers, MD (quoted elsewhere in Dr. Labor's text) is wont to say:

"Congratulations. You're fucked."

It is quite a story, and I am so lucky to have had a part in it.

Margaret Jarvis, MD
Chief, Addiction Medicine
Geisinger Health System

Distinguished Fellow
of the American Society of
Addiction Medicine

# INTRODUCTION:

Addiction is everywhere. You can't turn on the television or look at social media without seeing something about it. With the recent increase in opioid related deaths, you can no longer turn a blind eye to it, as the next one to fall could be your mother, father, sister, spouse or child. No one is immune. But what is addiction?

The Addictoholic Deconstructed has been designed to explain the disease concept of addiction in a concise way, littered with anecdotes from my own life and professional work with addicts. This book is NOT for people looking for a quick fix or easy solution for addiction, nor is it for individuals looking for an intense and scientific exploration of neuroscience. This book is for everyday people that just want to understand why addicts can't just stop.

As a recovering addict and a Board Certified Addiction Medicine physician, I like to think I have a wealth of both 'inside' and 'outside' knowledge on the subject of addiction. I have spent the better part of my career taking the information I have learned, and reformatting it into something that everyone can understand. I spend countless hours educating addicts and their families as well as communities, healthcare providers and other treatment providers about the disease of addiction. I am known for explaining the rationale behind current treatment modalities. This information has been widely received and acknowledged as being "the best presentation I've ever heard about addiction" by professionals and community members alike. That is likely the most 'tooting of my own horn' that you will encounter in this book.

My promise is that if you read this book, you will end up with a solid understanding of the disease and perhaps a bit more compassion for the addict, even if the addict is you.

ONE:

## WHY TALK ABOUT IT?

*"Fuck medical school,*
*I will just be a junkie for the rest of my life."*

- Me
(In one of the most stupid
and profound moments in my life)

At one point in 2005, I was sitting in my car, under a bypass in Irvington, NJ. My boyfriend and I had just copped some much needed dope. I had just pulled my dull ass needle out of my arm, dropped my head back into the seat and uttered the stupidest and most profound statement of my life. "Fuck medical school. I am just going to be a junkie for the rest of my life." This uncharacteristic sentiment tumbled out of me because the heroin just relieved the hours of horrific pain and withdrawal that came with not having it. It was like the moment a fan turns off, and the room is suddenly blissfully silent, but you didn't even realize the noise was making you tense. Not a crazy rush of pleasure, or euphoria. Not anymore. Not this far along. It was just relief. That relief was so all encompassing, so welcome, that I was willing to forgo a lifetime of ambition and hard work just to stay in that moment. There was no acknowledgment that the drug use had created the problem, only that it removed it. Temporarily. Now I could think straight. Now I would use my clear(er) head for the real work, the important work: finding a way to make sure we had enough money and dope to not have to feel that again. Withdrawal from opiates is like the worst flu of your life. There is nausea, vomiting, and diarrhea that seem like they are completely out of your control. Muscle aches that make even the strongest among us feel weak and helpless. There is this crippling pain, like someone scraping your bones with butter knives over and over. So yeah, finding a way to not have to feel it again was top priority. What I didn't realize in that moment, though, was that this day and that statement would signal the beginning of the end of my active addiction.

People are dying. People are dying of a disease that is preventable and treatable. But we can't prevent it if we don't know what it is. We can't treat it if we don't understand it. We won't seek to know or understand it if we can't eliminate the stigma. The stigma that says it's all about bad people making bad choices. The stigma that says only a certain type of person, from a certain type of home or neighborhood could be afflicted. The stigma that implies, in a deadly misperception, that it can't happen to me or you or us.

Addiction is a plague. It touches nearly everyone. It does not discriminate. It doesn't care if you are poor or wealthy, employed or unemployed. It doesn't care what race or ethnicity or religion you are. It affects atheists and zealots alike. It affects the young as frequently as the old. Parents and children and siblings and spouses are not exempt. It affects employees and employers, bricklayers and politicians. Police officers and judges and nurses and secretaries fall ill with addiction. It will infect stay at home moms, CEOs and bus drivers. And it most certainly gets its deadly claws into medical school students from good homes.

I am talking about addiction and the disease process of addiction for several different reasons. Aside from my own history with it. One of the reasons that irritates me both personally and professionally is this idea that people call addiction a disease, but really have no idea why. Some people (corporations, pharmaceutical companies, healthcare industries) call it a disease because there is some, though not much, money to be made. But if you ask many of those entities to explain what the actual disease is: Crickets.

There are some that will call it a disease because, bless their bleeding hearts, they need to believe that the addict has no choice in their fuckery and tomfoolery. Still there are others who have some inkling of an idea that maybe biologically there is something going on that is more than just terrible people making terrible choices.

For the most part, what I have realized throughout my career is that when I am asked to speak about a specific topic related to addiction, the questions that I am asked following the lecture are really indicative of the fact that people just don't get it.

Another reason I choose to talk about this is that I believe addicts need to understand what is going on within themselves. As much as we love to condemn an addict, no one, and I mean NO one is better at condemning them than they are. Addicts will beat themselves up, but then keep doing the same thing, and not know why. I want them to have love and forgiveness for themselves. I want family members to stop taking everything their addict does so personally. I think talking about the disease may give them a way to do that. Addiction is a conformational change in the brain that renders the individual unable to stop using substances without help. The symptoms of the disease range all the way from neurological underactivity to overt behaviors. The change does not occur in everyone that uses substances, but for those that do experience this biological rewiring, it can be devastating.

The stigma around addiction in society is nearly insurmountable. This negative portrayal of addicts in need of treatment and understanding ultimately limits access to services and the ability for addicts to thrive in recovery. It starts with our words and how we talk about addiction.

We are saying addiction is a disease, but when people begin comparing it to other disease processes like cancer or diabetes, it becomes a pissing match over which diseases are more important or deserve more attention. Because there are so many choice elements to it, it becomes harder to have compassion for the behaviors we see with addiction. I do not think I have ever witnessed someone say "I have multiple sclerosis" followed by a handful of people rolling their eyes, someone else walking out of the room, while another person announced, "My mom has cancer and she is a good person. Now THAT is a disease." Additionally, every time a diabetic dies from a seizure, ketoacidosis, or kidney failure because of how they chose to eat, there is nobody talking about how their kids are better off without them. Every time that I have been present when it is announced that an addict dies of an overdose, there is someone with an opinion about how their kids are better off. We only selectively show sympathy for the family members and loved ones of someone who dies from addiction because we only semi buy into the idea that addiction is in fact a disease.

T W O:

# IT ISN'T A NEW PHENOMENON

*"The best time to plant a tree was 20 years ago.*
*The second best time is now."*
- Chinese proverb

When I started partying harder than the average bear, sometime in my late teens or early twenties, there were a few unwritten rules. You don't smoke crack, you don't use heroin and you never used needles. Those were the 'dirty' drugs. That was the shit you did when you had a problem. Well, until you did those things. Then the only problem was getting them. You knew that these were the bad things. Maybe from D.A.R.E. Possibly after school specials. Might even have been Degrassi Junior High. For me, though, I can't remember when this transition occurred. One day I was washing the coating off of an oxy 160 (yep, back when those were a thing) and the next, I'm brandishing a needle, shooting heroin, smoking crack.

It is like when you are trying to lose weight. You start eating right and exercising and for a few weeks you are still running past the mirror naked, but then, one day you wake up and BAM! Your pants are too big and you check out your fine self for like twenty minutes from every angle. Obviously the weight loss did not occur in that one night, but we don't notice tiny changes until they add up to a big change. Our brains are way too busy noticing other things.

I remember the first time I met an actual drug dealer to buy drugs (instead of just getting them from a friend of a dude that my friend's friend knew), I insisted we meet in the fast food restaurant parking lot at 2pm, because, fuck, this is a drug dealer. They have guns. By the end of my active addiction, I would meet the dealer in the darkest alley I could find at 3am so the cops wouldn't find us. Because, fuck, cops. They also have guns.

The point of that story, though, is that back then, heroin was not something you came across at the grocery store, and it sure as shit wasn't available at every party. Today, the shift from using pills to using heroin is much less discernible as it is a more natural transition. Kids today have no idea how hard we had to work for our heroin. The distances we had to go...uphill, both ways, in the snow... or something like that.

It's important to note that in the United States there has been an ongoing epidemic of the disease of addiction for a very long time. Policymakers and society in general tend to view specific drugs as problematic rather than viewing the picture as a whole.

In the mid 1800's, morphine was prescribed to everyone for everything. Morphine is a powerful opiate derived from the poppy plant. Morphine is a great drug that helps with physical pain and discomfort as well as helps with emotional distress. Weren't women being diagnosed with psychiatric illness for having opinions around that time? Yeah, morphine is good for that. It helps give some people energy to clean out their garage like they've been meaning to for twenty years. It helps make in-laws more tolerable. Eventually,it caused problems. Problems like physical dependence and withdrawal when stopped abruptly, financial problems when trying to obtain more and more, and social and relationship problems when one places the use of morphine over the concern of loved ones.
As morphine is apt to do[1].

Then in the early 1900s Bayer Pharmaceutical created heroin in an attempt to provide pain relief in a way that would not have

---

1 My editor says that I need to cite my sources. I am my sources. This entire section is made up of bits and pieces of information I learned, heard, was taught, over the course of four years of undergraduate study, four years of medical school, three years of residency, one year of fellowship and over eight years in clinical practice. I wouldn't have the faintest idea which source to use for which sentence. I accept full responsibility for inaccuracies or misrepresentations in the information presented. Furthermore, I accept that this may impugn my reputation as an author. I can, however, promise that I did not look any of this up and then pass it off as my own knowledge. Because plagiarism is wrong. And actual research is boring.

the same negative outcomes as morphine.[2] Prescription grade heroin was marketed, and again prescribed for all sorts of maladies. Including the same physical pain as well as emotional pain, hysteria and just general intolerance of the world at large. That also became problematic, as heroin is apt to become. There was a pretty significant epidemic of illicit heroin use in the 1960's-70's. However, it was primarily affecting minorities and people of color, so it was promptly ignored. As we are apt to do.[3]

Then, in the 1980s there was a cocaine epidemic which amounted to a significant number of people dying of cocaine related deaths, including a number of pregnant women and fetal demise (that's miscarriage to the common folk). If you don't believe me, you can read all about it. Not here. But somewhere[4]. But if you are lazy, like me, just ask any ER doctor or nurse that was working in the 80's. They remember. At that time, lawmakers and treatment centers focused on how to deal with this cocaine problem[5].

Later on, in 2005 we saw the methamphetamine problem rise and people were blowing themselves up making crystal meth in the shed in the backyard. Old ladies were clogging up the 911 lines reporting their suspicious neighbors. The show Breaking Bad was wildly successful. Local meth manufacturers, in general, were not.

2 I will not speculate on the purity of the intentions of the Bayer Pharmaceutical company at the time that heroin was created, marketed and prescribed. It is entirely possible that they truly wanted to help and it was not all about profit margins. I think. Maybe.

3 The irony of the dismissal of issues of social injustice mentioned in a sentence that quickly moves on, is not lost on me. I think the discussion on the racially motivated legislation we have seen over the years is one worth having. Just not in this book as it will take us too far off topic. It is important to note that many of the laws around drugs and drug use that are still currently on the books were created to criminalize minority populations with overtly racist and prejudiced motives. These discriminatory statutes have led to many of the stereotypes that we still see portrayed in media today.

4 There is an actual book, by the DEA, about the history of drug epidemics. You can read all about the crack cocaine epidemic in the DEA History Book, 1876–1990 (drug usage & enforcement),also available at the US Department of Justice, 1991, USDoJ.gov webpage: DoJ-DEA-History-1985-1990

5 Incidentally a decent read about both of the previous footnotes would be Reinarman, Craig; Levine, Harry G. (1997). Crack In America: Demon Drugs and Social Justice. University of California Press

We fixed this by creating the Combat Methamphetamine Act of 2005 which put pseudoephedrine (a key component in methamphetamine) behind the counter at your local drug store. So now you need a driver's license to get cold medicine. Thank goodness we solved that problem. Around 2011, the bath salts epidemic marched in. There was a zombie apocalypse. It was all over the news that people were eating people's faces[6]. These bath salts were originally available at every truck stop and corner convenience store. The solution was to just stop those sales and create some lab tests to be able to detect it in the urine. It's almost like, I don't know, a pattern?[7] And then of course we have the curent-ish rise of opiates.

I could go into lengthy detail as to how this problem emerged. We know that there is a huge component of this that came from the Healthcare System and its underlying politics. But I would also say there's an equally huge component that comes from society at large and our over dependence on chemicals to fix any and all problems in life. There are some great books out there on the history of opioid overprescribing and the history of this opioid epidemic. I spend so much of my time dealing with addiction that I am generally not inclined in my free time to read about it. However, I did read Dreamland by Sam Quinonesand it rocked my world. It is such a great explanation of the rise of opiates. If you haven't read it, you should. After you read this one of course.

Two years ago I stood in front of a crowd talking about this 'epidemic.' I believe I was at an opioid task force conference and I said, "Hey, I really appreciate that we're here and we're focused on all the opioid overdoses, but mark my words, if we have enough of these conferences, in two years were going to see the rise of methamphetamine as opioids use will be decreasing." And as I write this in 2019 that is surely the case. Perhaps I knew because I am clairvoyant or maybe I have seen this pattern before. Probably the

---

6 National Institute on Drug Abuse; National Institutes of Health; U.S. Department of Health and Human Services. Also, see multitude of memes from that time re: zombies, cannibalism and bath salts in general.

7 This is not the first time we saw 'bath salts', although they went by other names and were available mostly as a club drug in the 1990's and early 2000. All the kids were 'raving' about it. You're welcome.

latter. Methamphetamine is on the rise. It's a different formulation of methamphetamine coming from other countries rather than being made in people's backyards. The current methamphetamine is causing pretty significant psychosis, sometimes with long-lasting or permanent effects.

As I intend to explain, the disease has to do with actual changes in the brain. And while a specific drug, or even behavior, may initially cause the change, once the change exists, all addictive drugs are a problem. In an individual, the disease is the actual brain defect and the symptom is behavior associated with that defect. Societally, the disease is the behaviors and the symptom is the drug du jour. Family members often come to me begging for help once they find out their loved one is using heroin. But when I elicit further history from them, there is usually a history of opioid pain pill abuse prior to the heroin. This almost always gets minimized, with a fixation on the drama of heroin. My point is, as a society, even as treatment providers, we keep playing the whack-a-mole game. You know, that game where you bop one mole down and then another one pops up and you try to bop that one. What we really need to be focusing on his how do we unplug the machine? How do we stop the game altogether? Because the problem is addiction. The problem is not a specific drug. We focus on how to treat the disease, not the drug.

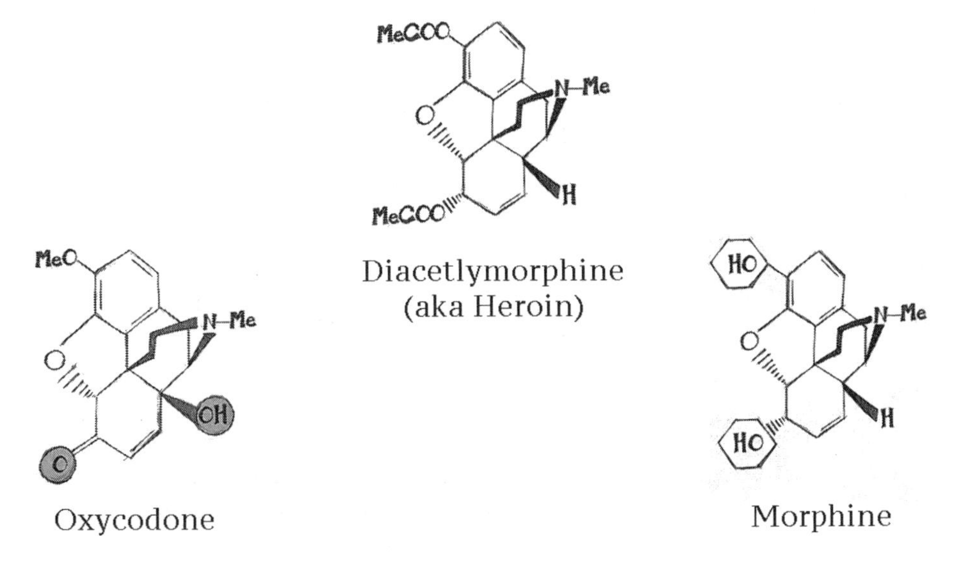


Diacetlymorphine
(aka Heroin)

Oxycodone

Morphine

THREE:

# A DISEASE or NOT A DISEASE

*"Sometimes, I've believed as many as six impossible things before breakfast."*

-Lewis Carroll,
*Through the Looking Glass*

In college, I am certain there were some lectures about partying too hard. I am certain I ignored them, however, I think they were ignorable. That is, those talks or lectures almost seemed to carry with them either the same preachy tone as the D.A.R.E. program in 5th grade or else the elitist cloak of 'at some point you will encounter those people'. There was never anything to sink your teeth into and there certainly wasn't any actual education about the disease process.

Medical school was no different. Before you assume I was too fucked up on drugs to properly remember, let me say this, you're right. But I did go back and ask a bunch of my non drug using classmates and they concurred. I also have all of my notes and textbooks. Well, not the textbooks. I sold those for drug money, but the notes were worthless on the streets, so I still have those. There is nothing about addiction. A little about alcohol withdrawal management. I found some mention of medical problems caused by long term alcohol use. And, of course, the infectious diseases lectures about IV drug users. But there is next to nothing about why people used drugs and why they continued to use them when their lives were falling apart. Literally.

One of the areas that I run into a lot of problems with, or at least see a lot of argument around, is this idea that addiction is a disease. Like an actual, bona fide disease. What I have found is that there really seems to be two camps of people and they are subdivided.

There is the camp of people that firmly believes this is a disease. These pro- disease people can be divided into the uneducated and the educated; please understand that the term 'uneducated' is not being used here as a judgment, it is simply describing those, 'without specific education'.

The uneducated pro-disease people say it's a disease, primarily because someone they respect or something they read and deemed valid, told them so. Without any education beyond that, this group tends to think that that means there is no choice at all and the addict should be absolved and excused from any and all wrongdoing. Then there is the educated group of pro disease believers who actually feel that there is a neurobiological component to this as well as a very strong genetic component that the person has very little, if any control over. However, in this particular camp of believers, most believe that an addict has some control of their behavior. I am a card carrying member.

Within the anti-disease camp there are also two categories. The same two categories, educated and uneducated. Again, no judgment. The uneducated group seems to really just think that calling it a disease is some sort of cop out. They attribute the disease label as some way for people to not have to feel bad about choices that they're making.

The second group is generally an educated group and they tend to propose that addiction is not a disease, but is any number of other possible scenarios. It has been called another form of PTSD. It has been called a learning disorder, as well as a purely spiritual malady. But most of the proponents of these theories are firmly adamant that it is NOT a disease. What I have found is that the people who tend to eschew the idea that addiction is a disease in favor of one of these other concepts seem to struggle most with the idea that if there is a disease, the person no longer has control or agency over themselves. That is to say that if we label addiction as a disease, then we take away a person's ability to fix or change it. I find this argument fascinating.

I think that this ties back into that whole concept that again we're calling it a disease, but not treating it the same way. For example, we all can acknowledge that Diabetes Type 2 is certainly a disease. However, huge numbers of people who develop this disease have done so as a direct result of choices they've made in their life. In order to treat their diabetes they have several options. They can certainly get prescribed medication if that's appropriate, but they may need to adopt some serious lifestyle changes as well as or in place of medication. Anything from checking their blood sugars to following up with the doctor more frequently, all the way to counting carbohydrates, monitoring everything they eat, incorporating some sort of exercise into their life and possibly seeking counseling for the depression that may have occurred with the diagnosis of the disease. Yet with all of this agency and ability to control how their disease process goes, nobody is denying that this is actually a disease.

I believe that the disease of addiction is truly a disease with biological and genetic components. In fact, it is these components that qualify it as a disease. Just as any other disease, there are huge components of action and work that need to come into play in order for this disease to go into remission. I do believe, that in part, it is a learning disorder. I believe that it is a dysfunctional skill-set as well as a spiritual malady.[8] I believe it has components of PTSD. But I also believe that there are significant disease processes occurring at different levels of the brain. And I do not believe that these must all be mutually exclusive.

---

8 Search amazon for books on addiction. Read the descriptions. You'll see. It is called all sorts of things besides a disease.

FOUR:

# DEFINING DISEASE

*"I don't care what you think of me.*
*I don't think of you at all."*

– Coco Chanel

We are very sophisticated in the world of medicine. Since the dawn of time, we have been working to understand the human mind and body. During the era of ancient Greek medicine there was a medical model was called the Humoral model. This model basically looked at the idea that there were different humors running throughout the body that needed to be released or replaced to stabilize the system. Throughout different times in history, medical practices involved bloodletting and things like drilling a hole in the skull to allow demons and certain other nefarious parasites out of the body in order to heal it. Over time, we moved on, and we learned more anatomically and micro-biologically. Models changed over time based on the information that was ascertained and what civilizations were capable of doing.

Eventually, the medical model progressed into the current model, which we call the Disease Model. In the world of medicine, in order for something to qualify as a disease, it has to fit into what we called the Disease Model. Which I know is a super fancy term. The disease model basically says that in order for something to qualify as a disease there has to be an organ, a defect in that organ, and symptoms that resulted because of that defect. In the example of type 1 diabetes, the organ is the pancreas. The defect is a decrease in beta islet cells. The symptoms are high blood sugar, diabetic ketoacidosis, retinopathy, and nephropathy. Now the question becomes how does addiction fit into this disease processes? We start with the organ, the brain.

In the 1950s and 60s, addiction was considered to be a moral failing. It was said to be only a sociopathic personality disorder - one that only affected those that were immoral or did not have a sense of right and wrong. Or it was attributed to some sort of specific environment, generally only affecting those of a lower socioeconomic status or lesser educated individuals.[9] A couple of researchers named James Olds and Peter Milner started doing experiments on rats, where the rats were able to administer stimulation directly into their brain. When the rats discovered the lever would deliver this stimulation, they would not eat or drink or play with the other rats or do anything that rats are supposed to do. Instead, they would just administer this stimulus over and over until they died. They ignored all their rat responsibilities. But they don't come from bad homes. They don't even have a prefrontal cortex, so it's not a matter of morals or ethics or values. This was the beginning of the study of the neurobiology of addiction.

Drugs, particularly any drug that is addictive, including alcohol, stimulants, benzodiazepines, barbiturates,opiates and tetrahydrocannabinol (THC)[10], all demonstrate effects in multiple areas of the brain. However, what they all have in common is that they work in the midbrain. Specifically, they act in the reward centers. This has been primarily determined in laboratory studies. Several different universities and labs around the world are looking at all the different aspects of addiction. In particular, they are studying the brain via imaging and post-mortem autopsies. It has been found that one is able to determine in what way a brain that has the disease of addiction differs from the brain of somebody who does not. These changes are repeatable, predictable, and thanks to technology, visible.[11]

---

9 This is where the stereotypical distinction between alcohol addiction and drug addiction started to emerge. They are the same disease but because alcoholism so prominently affected people from ALL walks of life, it earned a higher status in the stereotype world

10 Marijuana, reefer, pot, weed, dank, schwag, dabs, 420, bammer, maryjane, dope...

11 National Institute of Drug Abuse (NIDA) and Substance Abuse and Mental Health Services Administration (SAMHSA) are great resources for all this research I am talking about.

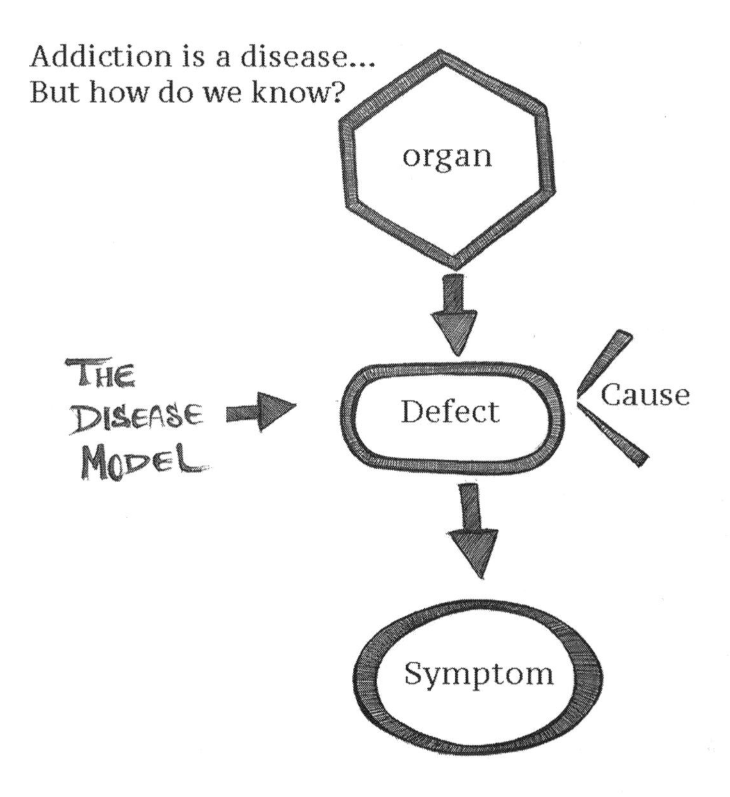
Addiction is a disease...
But how do we know?
organ
THE DISEASE MODEL
Defect
Cause
Symptom

FIVE:

# THE BRAIN...
# The Greatest Instrument
# We Will Never Fully Understand

*"The worst prison I was ever in was the one*
*I created based on what I thought you thought of me."*

-Kent C. (Anonymity and all)

When I was a little kid, my dad told me that I had to be either a doctor, a lawyer or an engineer. He was partly kidding. I thought an engineer was someone that drove a train, so that was out. In retrospect, I should have been a lawyer. But at that young age, I didn't really understand what lawyers did, except that there were lots of jokes about them. So I decided to be a doctor. It seemed noble. I wanted to help people. I also wanted esteem and prestige, though I had no idea what these things were. I wanted people to look at me a certain way. To respect me.

Much of my disease, the addiction, started long before I ever picked up a drug or a drink. It started with a maladaptive view of myself. I believed that defining myself was contingent upon what others thought of me. At a very young age, I learned that behaving in a certain way and presenting myself in a certain light, procured me a great deal of praise and attention. Being unemotional got me described as strong. When I was in kindergarten, I learned that if I said I was sick, I got extra attention from the teacher. I remember distinctly that when my best friend actually vomited up her grape juice in class, I did not feel compassion or concern for her; I felt jealousy and attempted to make myself throw up.

On the other hand, I learned that if, when my mother asked how I was, I told her I was 'fine,' that she seemed relieved and could focus on other things. I didn't want to worry her. Without realizing it, I was manipulating other people's emotions in an effort to control the outcomes. No one told me that I didn't have the right to deny people their own emotions.

This probably resulted from a near pathologic sensitivity. I seem to have been born with my skin inside out. Not literally. But I was so sensitive to anything and everything that I suspect this subconscious manipulation was a way to build some walls. I remember every Saturday morning I would take out ALL of my stuffed animals to play with while I watched cartoons. Not because I wanted to play with them all, but because I didn't want any of them to feel badly. If my aunt sent me an ugly sweater, I would wear it. Partly so my aunt wouldn't be hurt and partly because I didn't want to hurt the sweater's feelings. So by the time my dad asked me about my future plans at the ripe old age of seven, I was pretty well solidified in the routine of trying to be impressive. As time went on and I realized that there were multiple areas of medicine to specialize in, I triumphantly and not surprisingly landed on the idea that I was going to be a neurosurgeon. The most impressive type of physician I could think of. I mean, literally when anything is difficult, we say 'it's not brain surgery'.[12] I am not a neurosurgeon. But my interest in the brain remains.

There are multiple areas of the brain that are involved in addiction, and of course the brain is a very complex organ. The interactions among these multiple parts, while important, are not necessary for everyone to understand. However, I do feel that it is exceedingly important that anyone who has to deal with addicts understand the very basics of the neurobiology.[13]So to begin, the two parts of the brain that are really important to understand are the midbrain and the frontal cortex.

The midbrain is part of the limbic system that is located deep within the brain. It is present in even the most primitive species and is responsible for a number of survival and basic functions, including memory and reward.

The entire brain is covered in curvy, wavy road map called the cortex. It is what we think of when we think about the brain. The area of the cortex near the front of the head, behind the forehead, is

12 We also say, "It's not rocket science" but I am bad at math so astrophysicists can go write their own damn books

13 And who doesn't have to deal with addicts? I have yet to meet someone who has never come in contact with addiction in some capacity

called the frontal cortex. This area is unique to humans and primates, with one part of this area specific to humans. This area influences strategic planning and decision making as well as multitasking. This is the area where your superpowers are located.

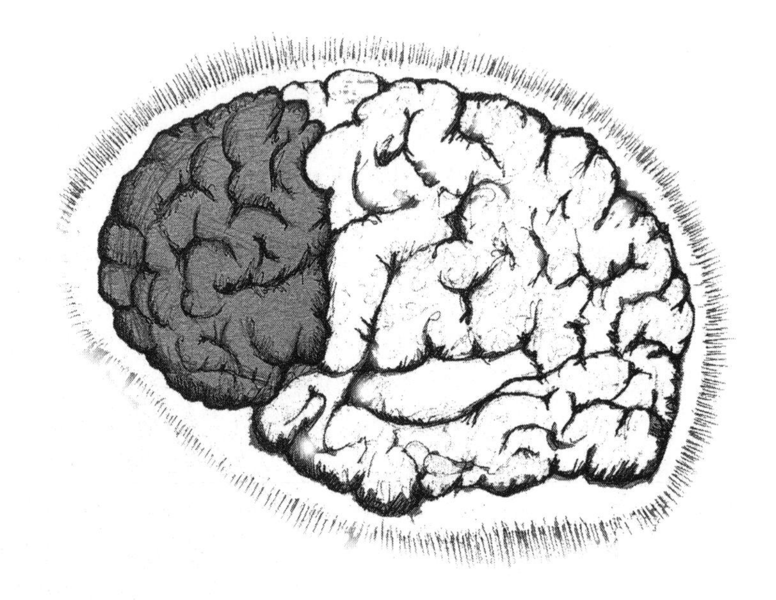

SIX:

# THE MIDBRAIN:
# A.K.A The TIGER

*"The moment you doubt whether you can fly,*
*you cease forever to be able to do it."*

– J.M. Barrie,
*Peter Pan*

Our midbrain essentially functions to keep us alive. The midbrain is a fight or flight, life-or-death processing station. The actions of the midbrain are subconscious. Whatever actions the brain deems helpful are reinforced by the reward system as a way to promote repetition of that behavior.

Basically, the midbrain has three functions: to eat nutrients and drink water; to fight off or run away from predators; and to procreate for perpetuation of the species. One of the first things we do when a baby is born is feed it. We do this because the nutrients in formula or breast milk will activate the reward system in the baby's brain. This will trigger the system to understand that these nutrients are now necessary for survival. We have no control over this part of our brain. We cannot fix it or change it or make demands of it.

I often use a picture of a tiger to represent the midbrain. A sleepy tiger would be a midbrain that is not active, that is not feeling threatened, that is currently satiated. The angry awake tiger is a midbrain that is feeling threatened, that is being chased by a bear[14]or that is feeling overburdened by the financial stressors of having just lost a job.

For anyone who has never been addicted to anything, imagine you are in the desert and you have not had any water for five days. Your organs are shutting down, you will not likely survive another twenty four hours without water. At this time, the midbrain is raging and active, and the frontal cortex is only minimally functioning.

14 Interesting fact: bears are natural predators of tigers.

If I were to come to you with a bottle of water and offer it to you, but tell you that if you drink it, I will take your children, job, bank account, home, etc., you would likely take the water. Because in times of extreme duress, humans will often behave in ways that violate their own core value systems just to survive. In this desert scenario, after you drank the water and the midbrain is satiated (at least temporarily), the frontal cortex reengages and you are flooded with guilt about giving up so many important things just for some water. You may try to manipulate me into giving you all of it back. You may berate or loathe yourself, creating a stress response, which will exacerbate the situation. And somewhere during your next twenty four hour pity party, you begin to experience the signs of severe dehydration again and when it is bad enough, you would offer to give up things you value for some more water. You would initially try to control what you are willing to surrender, but as you become more and more desperate and thirsty, you again succumb. This is similar to the process happening in the brain to an addict. Over and over. Throughout the day. Throughout the hour. But more on that later.

SEVEN:

# THE FRONTAL CORTEX: A.K.A THE SUPERHERO

*"The miserable have no other medicine but only hope"*
-Friedrich Nietzsche

The frontal cortex is a much more complicated area of the brain, and frankly there's much less understood about it. The frontal cortex is where a lot of our characteristics as human beings are located. For example, our personality, our ability to choose, our willpower, our ethics, our values, our morals, and our spirituality. The frontal cortex is also the location of any and all superpowers that we individually possess. If we happen to be particularly skilled at playing an instrument or a sport, there are pathways in multiple areas of the brain. Some have to do with our motor skills, such as, our ability to manipulate guitar strings or dribble a basketball. These motor skill pathways are built over time with practice. Other pathways are related to the complex processes associated with these skills, such as reading music or running plays on the basketball court. These are also built up over time. As these skills are becoming honed and improved, the pathways are strengthening and becoming more rapidly accessed.

Additionally, there's a skill pathway connected to the frontal cortex that is associated with those skill sets. Interestingly, we would not continue to pursue any of those things we are skilled at, if we did not get some reward in the midbrain from engaging in that activity. Which is why not every person loves to play the guitar. Or why not everyone that picks up a basketball for the first time finds it to be a super enjoyable experience.

Some of the other things that we have skill sets for in our frontal cortex would be coping skills and the ability to deal with stress. These are skills that need to be built up and developed over time as well.

I like to think of these skill pathways as similar to walking through the woods. At first, you walk through and you create a slightly trampled footpath. As you continue walking through the same path, over time, you wear down all of the foliage and it becomes a dirt bike path. As time passes, that footpath widens. Eventually, a horse can get down that path. Then, a car. In due course, it will get paved. Now it's a two-lane road. And ultimately, if someone continues to really hone their skills and ability, that pathway becomes a sixteen lane highway with traffic in both directions. If that person stops engaging in that skill for a long period of time, basically, a piece of yellow police tape gets hung up across that highway. With no one driving on it and no one taking care of it, the road eventually falls into disrepair. If, twenty years later, that person picks that instrument back up or picks that sport back up, the yellow tape just comes down and they are able to find their footing. However, that road is no longer safe to be traveled on and there needs to be a great deal of work in order to get it back to where it needs to be. This takes less time than building the initial roadway, but it still takes time and work.[15]

---

15 This analogy was used by my mentor, David J. Withers, MD, to describe addiction. I adapted it to the cortex. This man is by far the best storyteller I have ever had the privilege of meeting.

EIGHT

# SPIRITUALITY... WITHOUT ALL THE HYPE

*"It is only with the heart that one can see rightly; what is essential is invisible to the eye."*

- Antoine de Saint-Exupery, *The Little Prince*

Spirituality is a topic that comes up often in the treatment of addiction. This is primarily because of its role in the traditional twelve-step groups that are promoted for the treatment of addiction. However, it is also a source of controversy and probably the number one reason why people do not wish to engage in a twelve-step program. There is a very strong association between spirituality and religion and people seem to struggle separating these two concepts. Spirituality and religion are not synonymous. In fact, they even occur in two different areas of the brain.

Spirituality occurs mainly in the right parietal temporal region of the brain which is the part of the brain just over the right ear and back a little bit. The spiritual part of the brain is essentially our ego-centered area. The more active it is, the more a person is self-centered or focused on themselves and the less spiritual they are. People with high activity in this area would tend to be more concerned with doing what is best for themselves while ignoring the needs of others and reflecting statements like "this is mine" or "this is my opinion and why I am right." They tend to live in a state of the possessive, as in, they perceive the world from the most self involved view. In contrast, people who have developed a sense of spirituality, this area of the brain has significantly decreased activity. What that translates to is that these people tend to be far more" other centered." So somebody trying to find one's purpose in the universe and how it can be useful to all mankind or generally being of service to others would find activity in this area of the brain decreasing.

One of the primary ways of achieving this decreased activity is to engage in and develop spiritual concepts. Some of these concepts include developing a sense of honesty, integrity, faith, hope, love, trust, and willingness. Things that some call spiritual principles. Working on these spiritual factors generally will decrease the area in the spiritual part of the brain. Additionally, when an individual is working on developing these traits, and thus decreasing the activity in this area, they are more readily able to overcome addiction. While some people are best able to develop spirituality, or find their purpose, through religion, most are not. So a more secular approach is needed. Not to mention a less confusing situation. Active is bad, not active is good. Huh? Wtf, brain.

Just recently, some smart people from Columbia and Yale did a study where they found 27 healthy brained, non religious people. They found out what created a transcendent experience for each of them, then created a script for them. Participants were put in a brain scanner and given their script. What the researchers found was that no matter what the individual found to be a personally spiritual experience, whatever it was that caused them to feel connected to a higher purpose, lit up the same area in the brain.[16] So if your higher power is a tree, a park full of dogs, a group of other people or a God of traditional religions, when you think about it and feel connected to it, it's evident in the same area of the brain.

---

16 Neural Correlates of Personalized Spiritual Experiences, Lisa Miller, Iris M Balodis, Clayton H McClintock, Jiansong Xu, Cheryl M Lacadie, Rajita Sinha, Marc N Potenza Cerebral Cortex, Volume 29, Issue 6, June 2019, Pages 2331–2338

NINE

# NEUROTRANSMITTERS

*"We are the music makers and we are the dreamers of dreams."*
-Arthur O'Shaughnessy,
*Music and Moonlight*

Let's talk about neurotransmitters. These little guys are pretty much the bees knees when it comes to EVERYTHING. Here is how our brains work, super simplified times a billion.

Neurotransmitters are chemicals the brain makes as a way to communicate between neurons. They are made within each cell and stored in little vesicles until they are needed to relay signals about things like what is happening within you (your thoughts, feelings, or actions) as well as what is happening in the world around you. There are many different neurotransmitters produced, but some of the most common and most relevant to addiction are dopamine, acetylcholine, serotonin, GABA, and glutamate. I imagine most people would have heard of some or all of these.

Certainly around Thanksgiving[17] everyone becomes an expert in serotonin production because of the belief that when we eat turkey, which produces a precursor for serotonin called tryptophan, we become tired from serotonin's ability to relax us. Dads everywhere rejoice when their post feast nap was finally neurologically justified. This is factually inaccurate and isn't really happening, but we like to give the Dads wins where they can get them.

But back to the brain. For any action to occur, we receive a

17 As far as I know, Thanksgiving is an American holiday where we celebrate stealing the land from the Native Americans and the concurrent genocide of their people. Which sounds barbaric. So we fancy it up by saying that it is a celebration of family and the things we are grateful for. Canadians also celebrate Thanksgiving, which I think is a celebration of harvest. I have no idea if they are also celebrating genocide because I am a typical self centered American and know very little about any country other than my own.

signal that is either an electrical or chemical signal. An electrical signal would be something you see, hear, smell, taste. Maybe you just shifted in your seat without realizing it. But because one of the muscles in your butt was getting uncomfortable, it sent a signal to your brain, an electrical (touch) signal telling it to move. A chemical signal would be basically any substance that you put into your body. Chemical signals can be ingested orally, or by snorting. They can be put in via intravenous or intramuscular methods. They can be absorbed through the skin or mucus membranes or lungs. These chemical signals can certainly be drugs or medications, but also everything we eat or drink is a chemical.

Whatever the stimulus, the signal comes in and it tells that first brain cell that it encounters to "release the neurotransmitter." Whatever neurotransmitter is appropriate for that particular stimulus is then released into the brain space. That neurotransmitter is then picked up by the receptors designed for that particular neurotransmitter on the next brain cell. The receiving brain cell now sends a signal out saying "here is the effect."

An example of this would be, I am walking down the street and I see a hole in the ground. I receive an electrical signal through my eyeballs from the light of the sun, what I'm seeing visually, the contrast, the depth perception...and so on. That electrical signal triggers the release of a neurotransmitter. That neurotransmitter finds its receptor in the movement part of the brain and sends a signal telling my leg "take a step." That's how our brains work, again in a really really over simplified way.[18]

It doesn't matter what the originating stimulus is. What matters is what neurotransmitters are released and what their effect is. If I use alcohol or cocaine or heroin, it's going to tell that brain cell to release a bunch of neurotransmitters. It is those neurotransmitters that actually cause the conscious effect.

Let's imagine I use a stimulant such as cocaine. That cocaine molecule is going to bind to a brain cell that has a receptor for cocaine.

---

18 So if you are a neuroscientist reading this, first of all, why? Second of all, please save your comments about how I left out critical pieces for overzealous students and/or nerdy friends.

This will release stimulating neurotransmitters, and as they bind I will begin to experience an increase in energy and accelerated heart rate. I may begin sweating, and my pupils are going to dilate. Cocaine also releases dopamine into the midbrain's subconscious reward center. Dopamine is the pleasure chemical that, when released, tells me this is kind of good, I like this. This is comforting. It's enjoyable and I want to do it again, but again, all at a subconscious level. When I use heroin, I release a bunch of sedating chemicals as well as analgesic chemicals. This helps me get the intended pain relief and I may also get either sort of sleepy or experience an increase in energy. That effect has to do with the neurotransmitters that are released in the conscious areas of the brain, similar to the stimulating effects associated with cocaine. Heroin also releases dopamine into the reward center. Now remember, the brain actually makes the neurotransmitters, so the dopamine released from cocaine use is exactly the same dopamine released in heroin use. Alcohol same thing. Benzos same thing. This is why people can tell you "I know if I took this drug versus this drug" and why they might consciously enjoy one substance, but not necessarily another.

If that seems complicated, let me try to explain it another way. Some substances directly change the electrical charge of brain cells causing them to 'dump' the dopamine...a dopamine diarrhea, if you will. Other substances, like opioids, GHB, benzodiazepines and cannabinoids block the gatekeepers on both the entrance and exit sides of the brain cell so they lose control and dopamine can just start cruising around at will. Cocaine, amphetamines and ecstasy target the dopamine transporter, so they basically hijack the armored trucks that carry around the dopamine and they redirect them to wherever they want. While cocaine stops the dopamine truck from going back into its originating vesicle, so it hangs around longer. But amphetamines and ecstasy promote release of it directly from the trucks. Like an orchestrated oil spill. In all cases, dopamine levels in the reward center increase. (That was probably actually more complicated.)

In English, basically all that means is that ***all addictive drugs fuck with dopamine.***

What people using drugs don't realize is that at a subconscious level in the midbrain, all of those drugs are releasing the same dopamine, and dopamine is what we become addicted to. Are you picking up what I am putting down here? We don't get addicted to specific drugs; we get addicted to higher than normal levels of dopamine.

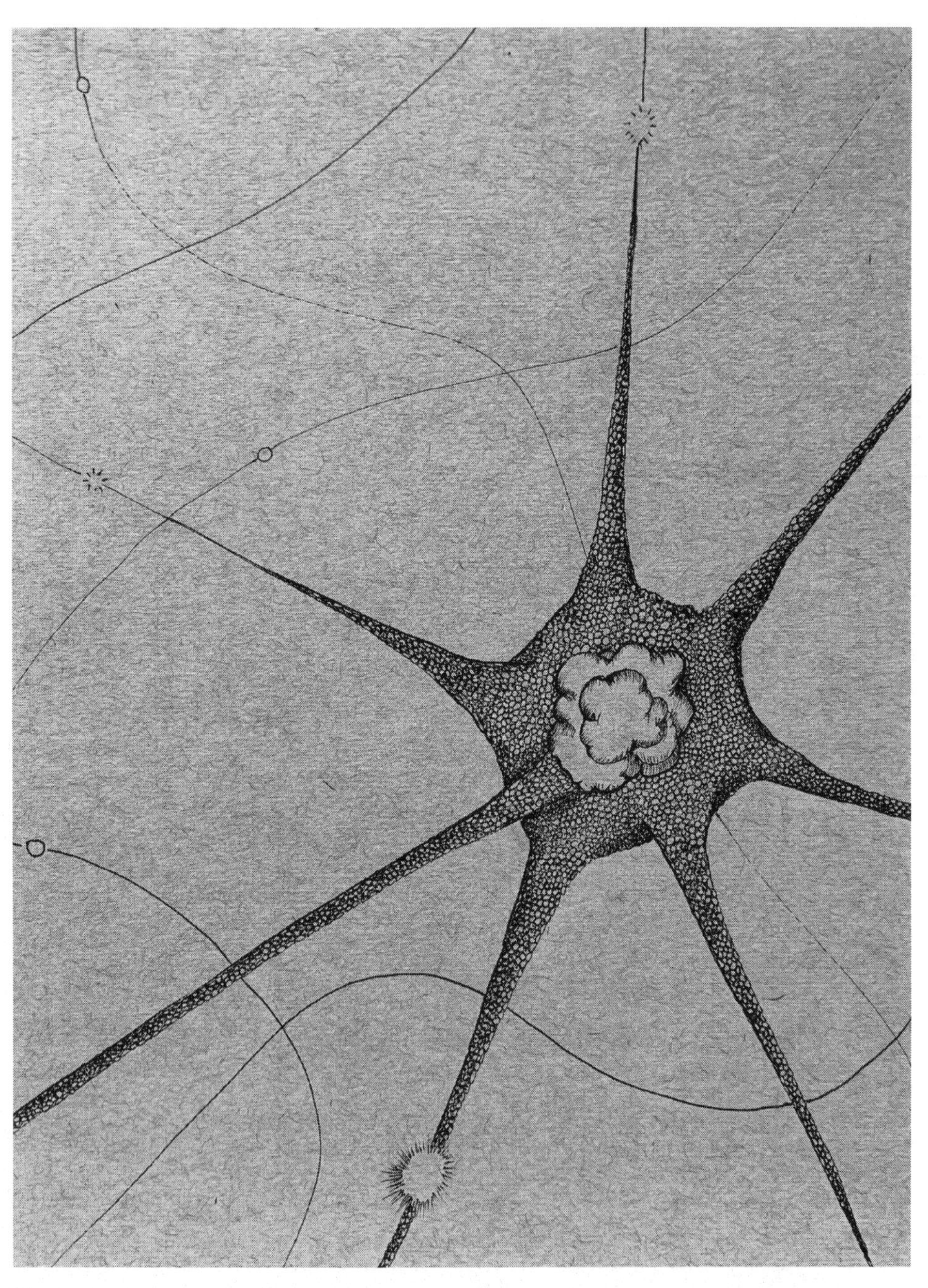

TEN:

## GET ON WITH THE DISEASE PROCESS ALREADY

*"If you hear a voice within you say 'you cannot paint,'*
*then by all means paint and that voice will be silenced."*
- Vincent Van Gogh

In the midbrain, we have a Reward Center and the reward center is mitigated mostly by the neurotransmitter dopamine. It functions to reinforce desirable behaviors. It does this because of a predetermined threshold for pleasure. Our threshold is determined by a number of factors including genetics and life experience.

All of the things that we enjoy naturally release certain amount of the pleasure chemical dopamine. The dopamine that is released in the reward center must be released in a certain quantity in order to cross our threshold and be recognized by the brain as a pleasurable experience. Remember, this is happening in the midbrain, so it is subconscious. Something that releases dopamine in an insufficient amount to cross my threshold will not be recognized as enjoyable. There are some general universals for people, for example, falling in love, having a child, getting a raise or a promotion. These things are usually enough to produce sufficient amount of dopamine to cross this threshold for most people. But there are certainly individual variances particularly when it comes to other activities. Personally I have no musical ability whatsoever. If I were to pick up an instrument right now and try to play, I would not find it enjoyable and I would not feel compelled to practice everyday to develop the habit of playing that instrument. Furthermore, if I were to pick up an instrument right now and start playing, no one around me would experience any kind of dopamine surge either, because it would not be an enjoyable experience for them. Trust me on this. The last time I attempted to do something musical was the day the dopamine died.

Our bodies and brains have an amazing capacity to adapt to situations. We all live at 97.8 (ish) degrees Fahrenheit. However if we get exposed to a virus or a bacteria our brain will change that set point to 101(ish) degrees Fahrenheit.[19] Because our body intuitively knows that at that temperature the bacteria or virus will be cooked and unable to replicate and will eventually die off. We, however, will not die at that temperature, provided we only remain there for a few days. Once the Invader has been eradicated, our brain resets our internal thermostat back down to the original 97.8. We had a fever as a result of our body and brain adapting to a situation. This adaptation can be seen elsewhere in the biological system and is critical to understanding addiction.

Chemicals (specifically drugs, alcohol or any abusable substance) cause the release of massive quantities of dopamine into the midbrain. When the reward center gets repeatedly exposed to these massive spikes of dopamine, it begins to adapt. The brain says, "Hold on, there is so much dopamine being dumped in here, we don't need to have all of these receptors for dopamine." Because the brain is a very efficient system. It doesn't want to expend a lot of energy maintaining receptors for dopamine.

Think of them like little cashier stations at Walmart. Not the self serve ones, the actual live-people-doing-price-checks-and-bagging-your-groceries-like-God-intended cashiers. Each cashier station has to be maintained and enough cash kept in each register, just as every dopamine receptor must be kept in working condition in order to accept and deliver the message of any incoming dopamine. Let's say that the store must make $1000 per hour in order to stay open. Each customer spends $10. They have ten registers open. So each register needs to serve ten customers an hour. Now let's say there is a huge sale and tons of customers start piling in. So management decides to close five of the registers so that those employees can go help the customers find things, restock shelves, etc. Now only five

19 This is because our bodies live in the most ideal condition for survival. It is called homeostasis. Also, we use Fahrenheit because just as we seem to be terrified of the metric system in the US, we also seem terrified of Celsius.

registers are open. So now twenty customers need to go through each register each hour to equal the same amount of money. However, now that there are more customers, the store needs to buy more supplies, so the overhead, or quota, goes up to $2000 per hour. Now, the same five registers have to serve forty people in an hour. The customers are the dopamine molecules, the registers are the dopamine receptors and the $1000/hour quota is the threshold. This means we have a higher need for dopamine in order to get the same pleasurable response. In essence, our threshold for pleasure moves up and we become unable to experience pleasurable things like we used to. This is because those activities are still releasing the same amount of dopamine as they previously had, but it's no longer enough to cross that threshold.

Ultimately we wind up needing chemicals or external substances in order to make us feel good. This is why anyone who knows an addict who is actively using, often times they will say he or she used to love to do something like play the guitar or play a sport, but they no longer do. They no longer really engage in any activity except the activity surrounding their use. That's because biologically they really aren't getting enjoyment from those things anymore. Their brain is just not capable of recognizing those actions as pleasurable anymore. We call this 'hedonic dysregulation' or 'pleasure deafness' or 'the Walmart Cashier Phenomenon'. Long story short, Walmart needs to keep more registers open.

When an addict says they are not using to get high anymore, that's legit. They really are not getting high. (Okay, sometimes they are getting high, but it is no more often than the non addict drinks or uses drugs to get high or 'party'.) They are using most of the time to just feel normal. Pleasure is needed for us to feel normal. Pleasure is a necessary phenomenon. Could you imagine waking up in the morning and having nothing to look forward to? As a species, we would have died off a long time ago if NOTHING was pleasurable (insert winking emoji here). If we never introduced food to the reward system of the baby, they would never desire or ask for food. They would die. Let's not kill babies. Let's acknowledge and appreciate the reward system. Even when it gets wacky.

There is a scenario where someone can use drugs for really long period of time and then just stop and never use again. That is not addiction. Addiction actually has to do with the conformational change in the brain. There has to be a biological change in the brain for it to be true addiction. I feel like this is where I get confused when people argue against the disease model. If you can see the brain, and you can see a defect, both in biological imaging as well as in the breakdown of behaviors, how is that NOT a disease process? Whether it is caused by the person themselves or by external forces, and whether it can be treated by the person changing behavior or by medication, it is still a defect in an organ. Now, if you put that person, the one who used drugs for a long time and then just stopped, in a brain scanner such as a functional MRI or a SPECT scan, and you put a true addict in the brain scanner, you could see the difference. You would see activation in the midbrain and a decreased activity in the cortex of a true addict.

There are a lot of people out there who like to say "just stop" or "just use willpower"or "why can't you just stop? I stopped. I used XYZ for ten years and just gave it up. All you need is to willpower." It does not matter how long you used nor what you used, if you don't have a gene for addiction or if your gene was not activated and the change in the brain that I'm talking about did not occur, you don't have addiction. The problem is, of course, we can't put everybody in the brain scanner and see if they are just using drugs or if they're addicted. That would be super expensive and honestly, not that helpful overall. Basically, if you know someone that was able to just stop walk away and never again use, that is awesome. But it is foolhardy and dangerous to assume that everybody else can do that. It is equally dangerous to assume that that same person could not, at a later point, activate a true addiction.[20]

When you view images of functional MRIs of the addicted brain, what we see is decreased cortical activity. We can also see

20 I, in no way, wish to diminish the magnitude of what these people accomplish. If someone is using substances for a long time and decides to stop, it is still very hard, even if they don't have the actual disease. If they are successful in stopping without any help, perhaps using only willpower and distraction, they are truly rock stars and should be commended. But they still were not biologically addicted.

that this decreased cortical activity extends beyond the point of just stopping the drug use. There's still a significant decrease in activity even with a hundred days abstinence from the use of the substance. Moreover, the change is constant no matter what the actual substance of the person was using was. If the person does nothing other than just abstaining from substances, over time we would see the cortical activity come back. This process, though, can take up to two years. For example, if we throw people in a jail cell and donothing else, when they get out they certainly have increased activity in the cortex, but they have not spent any time actually strengthening the areas of the cortex that would be necessary to fight off the urge to use again, should something stressful show up. I can't imagine that someone just getting out of prison could possibly face any stressors.[21]This is often why addicts will stop using for a period of a few days or a few weeks and insist that they don't feel any better. They say things like, "I might as well be using if I'm just going to feel this shitty all the time."

Shortly after I realized that opiates were, in fact, sort of, maybe a problem for me, I went to detox. I spent the first few days miserable and out of it. This was one of the most horrible experiences of my life, despite the pharmacy of medications they were giving me to 'help' with symptoms. They could've been skittles for all I knew. After the staff forced me to get out of bed and go to a group, I spent the next couple of days doing two things:

1.making sure everyone knew I was in medical school and going to be a doctor (because, again, it is all about creating a persona that is impressive. Nevermind that I am in detox. You can take your judgy wudgy attitude and shove it up your ass. You can call me Dr. Addict. Fuck you very much) and:

2. Trying to convince everyone of the thing I knew to be true at the core of my being... I was only physically dependent. If they could just get me through the withdrawal, I would never use again. I had no love for the drug.

---

21 Insert eye rolling emoji to indicate sarcasm

On my seventh day, I packed up my bags, took my little coin[22] and *Big Book*[23] and headed out into a world that felt like a cheese grater and I a piece of cheese. The physical withdrawal was mostly over, the sun was shining, my future was again bright...for about 2 miles. At which point, a shift occurred in my brain. My shiny new, detoxed brain. *Hey,* I thought, *I don't have to go through withdrawal if I only use occasionally. I will just be smart about it. There's no reason to give up using altogether, right*? And believe me when I tell you that this seemed like the most rational and logical thought I had ever had. I had so rapidly gone through the subconscious process of craving 'just one more' straight through to rationalizing, or 'green lighting' it. My willpower, fortitude and dignity were all left on the roadside less than three miles outside the treatment center where I had vowed to turn my life around.

In scans of the midbrain, specifically in a non-addicted brain, we see substantial activity where the reward system is located. In the addicted brain, however, we see significantly less activity. What this represents is the decrease in dopamine receptor activity (fewer cashiers/registers open). (Ugh! Again with the up is down, down is up bullshit.) This decrease in dopamine receptor activity occurs no matter what drug was being used and it persists through active addiction and beyond. It could take up to two years of abstinence from dopamine surges before we see dopamine receptors return to 'normal' numbers.[24] All addictive drugs will cause decreased dopamine receptor activity. When we are looking at this dopamine receptor depletion of the midbrain, it starts to become more clear that it doesn't really matter what the actual drug was. What matters is how the brain responds to it. **That response is the disease.**

The brain having decreased dopamine receptors is going to be

22 When a person completes a level of treatment or reaches a milestone in recovery, they are often given a coin or medallion with a number (months or years sober) or a saying such as the Serenity Prayer on it.

23 The Big Book of Alcoholics Anonymous is always referred to simply as a Big Book.

24 National Institute on Drug Abuse (NIDA)

the response if a person uses heroin or if a person uses cocaine or if a person uses Xanax or alcohol. This is hugely problematic because the change is universal and nonspecific. That is, it's not directly related to the specific drug. This presents difficulty with crossing addictions and believing that a different or other substances can be used in moderation because the brain's response, at the subconscious level, is the same no matter what drug is being used. So if someone who is addicted to heroin decides to stop using heroin and start drinking alcohol, the same decrease in dopamine receptor activity is going to occur. The brain is going to then need more dopamine, and that person is going to seek out a way to get it. So they are either going to start consuming large amounts of alcohol or they're going to wind up going back to the heroin.

It is important to note that this is not necessarily an instantaneous process depending on how long the addicted individual went without a substance before picking up the alcohol. But once they start using alcohol (or xanax or marijuana), the brain is utilizing that substance as the coping skill and a way to regain pleasure. And when a person is utilizing substances as their coping skill or pleasurable experience, they are not relearning or repaving those pathways behaviorally.

Addiction is a broken pleasure sense in the reward system. This part of the disease is not unlike cancer. In a normal system, we are creating new cells and killing off old cells on a regular basis. That's how our bodies are able to continue to live, grow and thrive. In cancer, what basically happens is that the cells of a particular organ or organ system start producing at a faster than normal rate and/or that organ or organ system is unable to break down or eliminate old cells fast enough to keep up with production. What we have is the creation of a tumor, or cancer. When the reward system, a necessary life system, is broken and becomes dysfunctional, that is addiction.

ELEVEN:

## OKAY, FINE,
## HOW DOES THIS EXPLAIN ALL THE SHENANIGANS

*"I can calculate the motion of heavenly bodies,
but not the madness of people"*

-Isaac Newton

Let's talk about craving. Craving is not like, "Oh my God I'm pregnant and I want a pizza." That is totally a thing, but it's not a craving. True craving is the psychological and physiological response created when the midbrain becomes active because it is feeling threatened. It is an overwhelming, obsessive need to feel different or to change the way that one is feeling in that moment. Depending on how extensive the disease process is, this can occur very frequently and in rapid cycles. Or for those in early recovery, there may be a very minuscule pause between this craving and the action taken.

In all my years of trying to explain addiction, I've never been able to come up with a really good analogy for what craving might feel like. I can tell you what it looks like from the outside. If you have a loved one who is an addict, you may have experienced something similar to the example I am about to lay out.

Imagine you have an addict who's been using heroin for some time. He or she decides to quit and asks for help. So you lock them in a bedroom with water and food and access to a bathroom for several days. They really go through it. They get sweaty and restless and achy and they're pooping and puking and crying. Maybe your heart goes out to them, or maybe you think well that's what they get. Either way after a few days, maybe three or four, they emerge from the bedroom. They're pale and a little clammy, however, you can see a little tiny spark in their eye. It's just a flicker of who they used to be but hope rises in you like a tidal wave. You think, "This is it, he's going to get it this time." He tells you that he's feeling pretty good and how grateful he is. Then he says, "I'm going to run down the street to the convenience store and get some milk," and your heart drops. You say, "No, no, I'll go. You stay here." And he says, "No, I really need to go. I might want a Tastykake also." You insist that you could get a Tastykake, but he insists that he doesn't know what kind he wants, and it would be better if he just goes, and that he really needs to get some fresh air. You continue to protest because you're terrified, but as you continue to protest, he continues to become more and more out of proportionately angry and defensive. He tries to appeal to your sense of logic saying things like, "After what I just went through, you really think that I would go and use again?" and, "Why can't you just trust me? I told you I wanted to get clean?" And finally, "You just want me to use so that you can feel like you're better than me." He storms out of the house. Maybe he returned three or four days or weeks later, actively using again. You are heartbroken again.

What's interesting about this scenario, is that for that person, for that addict, in that moment, he truly believes that he just wants to go to the store and get some milk and a snack. Subconsciously the midbrain is active, and it is driving him to just get out of the house. Remember the midbrain does not plan ahead or weigh consequences. It simply looks at the current situation and thinks of the quickest action to take to advance to the next step of survival. So in that moment, the midbrain, which is actively craving some dopamine, is thinking *step one: we gotta get out of this house*. Consciously, however, the addict just knows that they don't feel well, that they don't feel comfortable, and that perhaps a walk and a snack will relieve the discomfort. However, the moment that person steps out of the house and heads to the store, the midbrain will start the process of directing him towards the last place he could get dopamine.

While the argument could be made, that this is the moment when the addict has a choice, what the addict cannot choose is whether or not he is craving. He cannot choose to stop feeling that extreme discomfort because he does not even realize what the source of it is. True craving is equivalent to true suffering and nobody is choosing to suffer. Without adequate behavioral skills to combat that suffering, an addict will ultimately use.

Here's where shit gets real. When the midbrain is active, in that craving state, the frontal cortex shuts down. Well, it decreases activity and becomes weak. The skill pathways that the drugs are replacing not only get weaker (thinking, coping skills, stress relief, etc), but in the actual moment of craving, the cortex is paralyzed. Now, remember I said the cortex is where your super powers and skills and such are. The cortex is also a library of information about you. Everything about you is stored in there somewhere and catalogued. So when a craving comes on, the tiger wakes up as the library closes for lunch. The midbrain, like a ninja, sneaks into the cortex and starts going through the files looking for something, anything, that will justify using. Maybe it is a chronic pain problem. Maybe it is a dusty old anxiety problem we forgot we had. Maybe it is a situation or stressor that we haven't been stressing about enough like a job we hate or a family that never shuts up and wants to be in your business all the time even though you worked really hard to set up boundaries with them. Or, you know, whatever. So the ninja tiger midbrain takes that file and holds it up to the light so when the craving passes, and it always passes,[25] that file is staring us in our proverbial conscious faces.

When we are faced with this file, we are suddenly struck with the notion that it is legitimate and viable as an option to use. Before I give an example of what this might look like, I want to take a minute to talk about willpower. The old archenemy of impulse.

Lots of people want to cite willpower as the end all be all solution to addiction. But here is how willpower works: if I am at a red light, I keep my foot on the brake. I am physically capable of driving through a red light. I know that if I do so, I may cause an accident, I may kill or injure myself or another person, or I may get a ticket. So, willpower keeps me from going through the red light. Willpower keeps my foot on the brake. However, when the light turns green, I now have permission to drive through the traffic light.

25 Cravings generally pass with time (about 10 minutes) or with use of substance. In actively using addicts and/or early recovery, they come right back. Some could say that recovery is just a longer and longer pause between craving and action until that pause can be filled with productive things that don't involve using.

So all the willpower in the world, is rendered useless, because I now have permission to go. I do not need my willpower to hold me back from something I am allowed to do.[26]

When the craving passes and we are faced with the file that it found, we start the process of evaluating whether that file is giving us permission. For example, I may think, *you know what? I need to support my family. What good am I if I can't support my family? I can't do that if I can't work. I can't work productively if I can't sleep. Therefore I need to take Ambien, or drink a glass of wine, or take a oxycodone in order to be able to sleep. So that I can go to work. So that I can support my family. So that I can be useful.* Up to this point, willpower was most likely what was keeping me from using, but once this process occurred, I had a green light. My willpower is useless. The entire bucket full of willpower that everyone wants to say that I don't have, is full and in working order, but useless.

---

26 Analogy also stolen from David J. Withers, MD. No need to reinvent the wheel, amiright?

TWELVE:

## PEOPLE and PLACES and THINGS, OH MY

*"Three things cannot be long hidden:
the sun, the moon, and the truth"*
- Gautama Buddha

Let's take a moment here and talk about glutamate. Glutamate is the most abundant neurotransmitter in the brain, and it is responsible for laying down memories of positive experiences. I like to think of glutamate as the executive assistant to dopamine; the Ivy League educated executive assistant. Every time dopamine gets released, glutamate pays close attention to what caused it, and makes a note of it. Then, every time that same event occurs and dopamine is released, glutamate takes note of the things surrounding that activity. For example, if you take an oxycodone and your brain releases dopamine, glutamate makes the note 'oxycodone is awesome.' The next time you take it, glutamate notes 'Oxycodone comes in an orange bottle, orange bottles are awesome.' Then, 'The orange bottle comes from the guy with the white coat, white coats are awesome,' and, 'This building where the white coat guy works is awesome,' then, 'This street where the building is located is awesome,' and so on. Similarly, this is why if you are going on vacation to the same place every year, just packing your suitcase for the trip releases a little bit of dopamine, in anticipation of the larger amounts of dopamine soon to be released.

I can't tell you how many times I was sitting in my car, dope sick and terrified I was going to go into full blown withdrawal. But when the dealer would call, and his name was always a letter, like "L" or "D" or whatever, when I saw his 'name' pop up on my phone screen, I would instantly feel about 10% better and by the time he actually arrived, and I saw his face, I was probably 30% less sick. This was all before I even laid eyes on any drug. There is no denying that opiates cause physical dependence, so there was no doubt that my withdrawal was not 'all in my head', yet, just anticipating getting the drugs was enough to give me a small amount of relief. Such is the power of glutamate.

Just as the sight of a drug dealer or the bar where one always drank can elicit powerful physical symptoms, the repetition of certain behaviors associated with drug and alcohol use can be problematic. Let's say that every time an addict was dishonest, they were able to get drugs (or money for drugs). Over time, dishonesty starts to be linked (Thanks, glutamate!) with the pleasure of using the substance. Soon, dishonesty itself allows a small amount of dopamine to be released. Even if the lie has nothing to do with getting or using drugs. Many addicts will tell you that in early recovery, they will often 'Lie just to lie.' I distinctly remember telling someone, my boyfriend or maybe my mom, that my shoes cost $40 when they actually cost $30. For absolutely no reason. They weren't going to give me the money back or go buy them themselves. It was just so natural and easy to lie, and so uncomfortable to be truthful, about anything.

There are a number of other things that start to get linked to addiction in addition to lying. These behaviors themselves become part of the problem and part of the feedback loop. In the above example, every time I told a lie, whether it was a 'useful' lie or not, I got a small amount of dopamine released in the reward center, which cataloged the act of being dishonest as 'pleasurable' making it more of a default than being honest was. So now dishonesty is part of my disease process.

Another example of the habits of the disease becoming part of the disease can be seen with instant gratification. When a person uses drugs, they receive the satisfaction of instantaneously (or close to that) getting the intended effect. Because this instant effect is associated with the 'pleasurable' act of using a substance, instant gratification itself starts to be viewed subconsciously as pleasurable. The brain will then reach for instant over delayed gratification more and more even when it is not related to substance use.

This causes two noticeable outcomes:

1. Addicts have little to no patience for anything and become entitled and demanding and

2. The constant use of instant reward as a coping mechanism causes the deterioration of the skill pathways for coping (remember the highway falling into disrepair).

So when we start looking at treatment (and we will, I promise, just be patient), we have to look at how oftentimes it is the small things that really have the most impact, and we have to start 'rewiring' a lot of these maladaptive behaviors.

This whole dysfunctional process is made worse by our cultural belief that we need to instantly and chemically fix any and all problems. The number of prescription drug commercials we are bombarded with on a daily basis borders on harassment. It is a running joke that if you take medication A for headaches you will have nausea, heartburn, chest pain, shortness of breath, worsening of heart failure, complete failure of your kidneys, death, revival and death again, toenail fungus and an impending sense of doom as well as worsening of the headaches you are taking it for and then the next commercial is for a nausea medication with a similar list of side effects. This is what we promote. Not hungry? Take a pill. Need more energy? Drink this cough syrup tasting sugar water. Sad? Pill. Happy? Pill. As a society, we forget to give some grace to our bodies and allow them to (re)learn all the things they know how to do without a pill. Think about it. If every time you need to sleep, you take a drug, illicit, prescribed, or over the counter, your body and mind start to say, "Fuck it, we don't need to remember the skill of sleep. This dude is just going to do it for us." Then, when we have to go a period of time without the chemical we are upset that we can't sleep.

As far as I know, and I acknowledge that I may be wrong because I am not going to look it up, there is only one disease that causes people to die from lack of sleep. It's called fatal familial insomnia. No one that I know has it. Now, I can acknowledge that some people can fall asleep quickly and easily (I swear I am asleep right no...kjgglj;'ljhiu711jfkdii lv l) Others, have a more difficult time. But even those that have severe insomnia, with ***time*** and ***practice*** of sleep hygiene behaviors, can and will sleep without medication. When I tell my patients this, I most frequently hear, "But it's not fair!" I'll get to 'fair' in a minute. But I show them a list of sleep hygiene behaviors that they need to do every day for at least two weeks consistently. Things like, no caffeine after noon, exercise every day for thirty minutes but not after 5pm, no napping, and no TV, computer, tablet or phone for two hours prior to bedtime. Go to bed the same time every night, get up the same time every morning. If you are not asleep in twenty minutes, get out of bed, leave the bedroom, sit in a chair and do a crossword puzzle, or draw, or read until you are sleepy. Try again. If twenty minutes later still no sleep, do it again. Do it all night. Even if you don't sleep at all that night, still get up at the scheduled time. Eventually, the body will regulate and sleep will become the norm rather than the exception. Is it fair that I can watch *Murder, She Wrote* episodes right up until the second my eyelids close and still be able to sleep, but you can't? Nope. Is it fair that a diabetic can't eat cookies and cake to their heart's content? Nope. Is it fair that the entire Kardashian family could afford to own a country even though they have no talent? Nope. My point is, that while it may not be fair, tough shit. That is life. Life is not fair and it never has been. But trust me on the sleep. In most cases, for my patients at least, it's not the sleep that is the problem, it's the need for instant gratification.

Isolation is another behavior that we see glutamate linking to pleasure. Most addicts have a small contingent of homies that they hang out with on the regular, and most of those are also actively using addicts. Avoiding people that care about us or that might have a negative opinion of our behaviors allows us to keep using and to use with less guilt. The first time I drank, I was about twelve years old, and I was at a party with my parents. A bunch of us kids had stolen a six pack and were sharing it. After it was gone, here is what I remember: I was not done. I continued to sneak back into the kitchen and take more and more beer. No one else was doing it with me. I started taking the beer into a closet I found so I could drink it without anyone saying anything. I did not spend any part of the night actually enjoying my buzz or socializing with my friends (who all seemed to have a good time despite their lack of excess alcohol), I spent it alone. In a closet. Just so I could keep drinking.

As I got older and moved through the various phases of 'adult' life, I physically moved further and further away from family and friends who knew me best. It was not conscious. I wasn't deliberately trying to live far away, but subconsciously the need to isolate myself from those that knew me was already rooted and associated with 'pleasure' in my brain. Living a distance away also lent itself to my need to create the image of myself that I wanted everyone to see. For me, this goes back to that need to control and manipulate everyone else's thoughts and emotions. Which, you guessed it, was tied (Thanks, glutamate!) to the pleasure of getting attention or preventing people from feeling their emotions.

Yet another area where we see associated behavior becoming part of the disease is with drama. And I don't mean a television mini-series. Because real life is so much dirtier than that. Often when an addict first stops using substances, their life descends into chaos. Not because of their legal and financial issues, although those contribute, but mostly because of relationships. Relationships with friends, spouses, parents, children, siblings, neighbors...you name it. Let's consider this. An addict has been isolating, avoiding, and stealing from her parents to support her habit. She also is controlling and manipulative because these behaviors serve her in some way, and over time they too become linked with the pleasure of using (Fuck you very much, glutamate!) Now we take away the drug. She no longer has the need to isolate and actually she needs her parents to help her get back on her feet. But she has only been abstinent for a few days or weeks, so none of the coping skills for life have been built up and none of the dopamine receptors have returned. So she is dysphoric - unable to experience feeling normal or enjoying very much. But she finds that throwing a temper tantrum every time her mom asks her what she needs to borrow the car for, is somehow... satisfying. Drama, friends. Drama is so closely tied with the life of using that it is often the only 'drug' that a newly recovering addict has to 'use.' Unfortunately it tends to make their lives and the lives around them utterly miserable and exhausting.

In the disease of addiction, the most problematic part is certainly the use of the actual drugs, but the behaviors that coincide, surround, and support that use can also be problematic. Just as the actual substance use gets worse over time, so does the dysfunction of these behaviors. While the actual disease of addiction may not occur until the changes in the reward system occur, the entire system can be primed long before that. And the most common primary catalyst for that is stress.

THIRTEEN:

## TRAUMA DRAMA

*"How do you know an addict is lying?*
*His lips are moving."*
*"An addict will steal your wallet and then help you look for it."*
-tired old cliches/jokes...
...with some truth in them.

There is a meme floating around right now that basically says 'Weed isn't a gateway drug. Alcohol isn't a gateway drug. Nicotine isn't a gateway drug. Caffeine isn't a gateway drug. Trauma is the gateway. Childhood abuse is the gateway. Molestation is the gateway. Neglect is the gateway. Rape is the gateway. Drug abuse, violent behavior, hypersexuality, self harm, etc. are often the symptoms (not the causes) of bigger issues that almost always stem from a childhood filled with trauma, absent parents, and abusive family.' I have no idea for sure who the original author of this is, but most memes attribute it to Russell Brand (whose book *Recovery: Freedom from Our Addictions*, about the 12 steps is fucking amazing). Stress and trauma are monster areas of study right now. The role of stress and trauma in addiction is undeniable, and you don't need a medical degree or even any knowledge of addiction to understand why. Even those without any substance use issues have had a glass of wine to 'unwind', taken a cigarette break after a stressful meeting at work, or snorted a line of blow at a party under the guise of 'letting loose' and 'relaxing'. When an individual suffers the loss of a loved one, doctors are quick to prescribe them some Xanax or Ativan to numb the grief and sadness.

Substances, particularly the highly pleasurable ones are quick easy fixes for stress. Even food, which is for all intents and purposes a chemical, is a quicker and easier fix than behavioral coping mechanisms. Unfortunately, for most of us, stress is not a one and done phenomenon in our lives. It tends to be chronic and repetitive. But our solution, to use a quick fix, is not a chronic solution. Herein lies part of the problem.

Let's start with stress and the brain. Many people are wired so that when we experience chronic and severe stress, our bodies produce a chemical called corticotropin releasing factor (CRF). Now this chemical has several functions, but we are going to focus on its role in the reward system. For evolutionary reasons far above my pay grade, when we have high levels of this CRF circulating in our brains, we respond by down regulating certain dopamine receptors. Did you get that? Our brains start taking away the dopamine receptors. So for those of you paying attention a few chapters back, this is the same thing that happens when people use drugs over and over. This is the Walmart Register Phenomenon, but instead of a sudden surge of customers causing the registers to close, it is a hurricane warning that warrants sending half of the employees home. The dopamine receptors down-regulate or are taken away because of stress. This means that people with severe chronic stress actually need higher levels of dopamine to feel normal and to enjoy life. We know that statistically one out of every four addicts has a history of trauma.[27] Trauma can be physical or sexual abuse, neglect, domestic violence, a really nasty divorce, loss of loved ones, combat violence... no one can tell you what is or isn't traumatic to you. Your brain will decide that for you.

Imagine that there is a child who is abused. That child never had the chance to build up any coping skill pathways in their brain to begin with, so they are starting with dense woods. They experience abuse, they produce CRF, they have decreased dopamine receptors. But they probably don't even realize that this isn't normal because they haven't known any other life. Now imagine someone gives that child of eleven years old a beer or a joint. That substance dumps a bunch of dopamine into their brain. For the first time, they feel normal, good, and safe. So they begin seeking out the chemicals that make them feel this way. Their brain starts to associate the use of these substances and feeling good with the relief of stress. It

27 Let's be honest. We all know it is higher than this. But this is what is reported.

catalogues drug use as a 'coping skill' and so they continue to use substances even if their life improves and the sources of the trauma are no longer an issue. Now, they have 'normal' life stresses... bills, jobs (or lack of), children of their own, etc. They are still using substances to cope with these smaller stressors. Now, they have a higher physical tolerance. So they need more to get the same effect. The brain responds to these increases in dopamine by further down regulating the dopamine receptors. Now, they really need the drugs to feel normal. But obtaining the money for them or procuring the drugs themselves becomes a stressor as well as hiding their use from family members, co-workers, neighbors. Now, the drug use is chronically stressful. Stress leads to addiction which leads to more stress. It is a vicious cycle.

On the flip side, if one in four addicts has a history of trauma, what about the other three? Well, for most of them, it did, indeed, start with a choice. However, with the exception of a few religious or cultural practices, I don't know a single person who has never had a drink of alcohol (and when we talk a little about genetics later, this will make more sense), and for some, it only takes one drink to trigger the addiction cascade.

So let's imagine there's an adolescent who has a drink with her friends at a party. They all drink some, but she notices that she really likes the effects and seems to be able to handle it better than her friends. Throughout high school, she continues to drink at parties and tries marijuana and maybe some hallucinogens. She gets into a good college where she continues to party in a way that seems comparable to her peers. Maybe she drinks a little more than they do, maybe she's always at the after party. Maybe she starts partying with different people on different days so no one really notices how often she is getting messed up. Her grades begin to slip. She tries to cut down on her drinking, but after a couple of weeks she always winds up going back to it. Now she is facing getting kicked out of school, plus she can't really afford her habit so she is forced to be creative to get her drugs and alcohol. She winds up moving back home with her parents and she can't get a decent job due to not having a degree, not having any skills and she finds herself night after night at the local watering hole. Her life has become a chronic stressor. While she continues to use substances to drown out the chatter in her head telling her she is a failure, her brain is cataloging the substance use as the coping skill for her stressors. The pathways for coping that she had started to build up as a young person, start to get neglected and fall apart. Soon her only coping skill left is to use. Her use led to chronic stress which led to further use. Behold, another vicious cycle.

In both scenarios, and everywhere in between, we can see the link between stress and addiction. The vast majority of successful treatment programs and modalities involve the learning or re-learning recognition of and coping skills for stress.

When addressing trauma and addiction, however, the addiction is the more acute problem. That is, we have to address the addiction first. Why? Because addicts have no coping skills. So if we put them with even the most skilled trauma therapist, and they start digging through the quagmire of their past trauma, how the fuck are they supposed to handle that? They will immediately reach for the only coping skill they have. This will lead to continued suppression of the emotions that they need to work through. Coping skills need to be put in place first and then the trauma work can begin.

When I was in treatment, I think maybe a week into the thing, I was performing my 'Look how well I am doing by trying to dig deep into my psyche' act when I said to a staff member *I think that if I can get to the root of why I am an addict (trauma) that would help me get clean.* She responded,"You don't have to know how to make a donut to eat a donut." She was saying that I didn't need to know the 'why' in order to fix it. That I actually needed to fix it first. Without a properly working coping system, I would never be equipped to deal with what I found. She was right, of course.

FOURTEEN:

# THE SKINNY ON GENES (NOT TO BE MISTAKEN FOR SKINNY JEANS)

*"I am not afraid of storms,*
*for I am learning how to sail my ship"*

-Louisa May Alcott,
*Little Women*

Disclaimer: I am not a geneticist nor a microbiologist. Nor any other kind of -ist that has a firm grasp on genetics and how genes work. I could probably do some research on it and try to break it down enough for me to understand it better, but I won't. Maybe for my next book. But here is how I understand it in very basic and rudimentary terms. We have lots and lots of genes. Genes are like little computer programs for individual traits and characteristics. These programs can be actively running or dormant. I, for example, have a program for brown eyes that is actively running. Some programs are never activated. So, I may have a genetic program for lung cancer, but if I never smoke or get exposed to a chemical that turns that gene 'on,' then I won't ever have the actual disease of lung cancer. If I don't have a program for lung cancer then I can smoke a million packs of cigarettes and I will never get lung cancer. I will probably not be able to walk more than two steps without getting out of breath and I probably would smell really really bad, but I wouldn't have lung cancer.

We have to have a gene, or program, for addiction. Most people have at least one of these programs. I think the real number is around 60% of all people have at least one gene for addiction.[28] Remember, genes can be passed down from many, many generations ago, so don't assume that because your parents and grandparents never touched a drink or a drug that you don't have a gene for it. I

28 National Institute on Drug Abuse (NIDA)

like to make up statistics because again, I am too lazy to actually find them, and also because the ones I make up sound better in support of whatever I am saying. So I usually tell people that it is close to 90% of all people that have a gene for addiction. The truth is that it doesn't really matter. Since we don't know if we have it or not, I think it is best to err on the side of assuming there may be one somewhere in that vast DNA code.

Now, each of these genes that we have need to be triggered or activated or turned on. It can be something specific that triggers it or something general. But once it is triggered, a cascade of events begins that is irreversible and quite frankly, the suckiest thing about it.

Lets simplify further, shall we? Let's say that Patient A has a gene for addiction but that gene is only going to be triggered by opiate use. And let's say that it actually takes fifty uses of opiates to trigger that gene. So Patient A starts out as a drinker. For ten years, every day after work he has a few drinks and usually drinks quite a bit more on the weekends. Then, one day he meets the lady of his dreams and she doesn't drink. They fall in love, get married and have some kids. Before you know it, Patient A has decided to put down the alcohol and focus on his wife and kids and good life. So for seven years he never touches a drink. He never takes any prescription meds or does any drugs. In fact, other than that one time in high school, he's never even smoked pot. Then, one day, Patient A is on a ski trip with his lovely family and he injures his knee. And he gets knee surgery. He is prescribed oxycodone. He has taken hydrocodone or oxycodone once or twice in the past after dental procedures, so he knows he isn't allergic to it. So he takes it for his knee pain, as prescribed. But by the seventh day he has taken the fiftieth opiate pill he has ever taken in his life and he starts to realize that these pills not only help his pain, but they also help his anxiety. They motivated him to start writing that book he has been talking about for years. They make him jovial at dinner time and his kids think he is suddenly hilarious. He calls his surgeon and says that he is still having pain. The surgeon knows that Patient A has a good job, a nice house, and takes his family on skiing vacations. The surgeon gives him another prescription. This goes on for a while before the surgeon starts to get suspicious and finally cuts him off. Patient A resolves to get through the withdrawal, but he didn't anticipate the severe anxiety and resentment toward the surgeon that he would feel. He didn't anticipate the cravings to use and then the justifications like, "I am making my family miserable. I just need one pill a night" or "I am nearly done with my book, I just need to keep taking it until I finish that." So he goes to a friend. Then a friend of a friend. He starts getting oxycodone from the streets. Eventually, his guy can't get any pills, so he is faced with the option of trying heroin. At first he says 'no way,' but as the physical and emotional pain become more and more fierce, he eventually succumbs. We all know the rest.

So Patient A winds up in detox with me. I explain that I can detox him from the opiates, but after detox, he can't use any substance including alcohol. He nods his head and says he understands, but in his head he is thinking "I drank alcohol every day for ten years. I put it down and walked away. Alcohol is not a problem for me. Dr. Labor is just being dramatic." A year later he is back in detox, but this time for both heroin and alcohol.

See, Patient A had a gene for addiction but it was never turned on by the alcohol. However, once he had enough exposure to opiates, it was turned on. Once it was turned on, it started the process of removing those dopamine receptors from the midbrain. Once there were fewer dopamine receptors and he needed more dopamine to feel normal, any drug that released higher than normal levels of dopamine would fulfill that subconscious need...including the previously innocuous alcohol.

Understand this, the dopamine that the brain is craving is released by all addictive substances. So once the gene is activated and the brain changes occur, all substances are problematic. Even ones the person has never ever used before or never previously cared for. Furthermore, as the individual continues to use substances to cope with everything, the brain loses the ability to cope with stress without substances. So when Patient A got out of detox, as soon as he was faced with a stressor, he reached for alcohol. Without realizing or thinking about the fact that for the seven years prior to the addiction, he had been perfectly capable of dealing with stress.

Consciously, though, he told himself he didn't have a problem with alcohol so it is an appropriate coping tool.

The genetic experience can really be summed up easily:

1. Particular addictions can run in families, sometimes many generations back.

2. Specific genes influence the rate of drug metabolism or the intensity of the effect (how much neurotransmitter is released) thus 'triggering' the changes in the midbrain to occur and

3. Certain genes can contribute to personality types that may predispose a person to use substances (think of a shy person using alcohol to be more social or a risk taking personality being more adventurous at a party where drugs are available).

This explanation, much like the neurotransmitter explanation, has been formatted to fit your brain and interest level. If your brain craves a higher level understanding of this stuff, please, go read about it from smarter people than me.

FIFTEEN:

# THE ACTUAL DRUGS:
# A BRIEF PRIMER on the SHIT THAT WILL FUCK YOU UP

"*Knowing is not enough; we must apply.*
*Willing is not enough; we must do.*"
-Johann Wolfgang von Goethe

This is addiction 101 not drug use 101, so I promise to get to the non-drug things you can get, too. But first I want to talk about the addictive drugs. I have no interest in talking about the pharmacokinetics or pharmacodynamics or chemical structures of these things. If you want to have a chat about these things, come on over some time and we can eat dry toast and drink lukewarm tea and I will share all that I know. But honestly, that is boring. I am going to talk about what they are and what they make people feel like. And I will add my saucy opinions as we go.

**ALCOHOL:**

Alcohol is the most commonly used abusable substance. I am talking about the drinking kind, not the rubbing kind (though the hard core alcoholics will drink that too. WARNING: DO NOT DRINK RUBBING ALCOHOL. YOU WILL DIE). Alcohol is responsible for more deaths than any other drug. Generally, with a lower consumption of alcohol, it makes people feel relaxed, uninhibited and fun. It can also lead to people feeling very emotional, disoriented, and with impaired vision, movements, and memory. Blackouts, a temporary loss of time and inability to form new memories, can occur while drinking. This greatly increases a person's risk for assault, robbery, and generally making a fool out of themselves. It also releases dopamine in the reward center.

There are many risks associated with alcohol consumption. If someone drinks more alcohol than their body is able to process, they can develop alcohol poisoning. This is a toxic state of basically fermenting one's self. It can lead to death. High levels of alcohol in the system works like a depressant, making someone drowsy and potentially leading to them passing out. If they pass out somewhere outdoors in either the scorching sun or below freezing temperatures, or in any body of water like a pool or bathtub, they can die. Alcohol intoxication can lead to death. If someone drinks alcohol daily for a period of about seven days or more, even just one beer, they are at risk for withdrawal. Alcohol withdrawal is usually comprised of sweats, chills, nausea, skin crawling, anxiety, vomiting, diarrhea, seeing or hearing things (like bugs, shadows, Great Aunt Mildred calling your name), weakness and tremor, or shakes. When withdrawal progresses to full blown delirium, where the person no longer can tell the difference between reality and hallucinations, it is called delirium tremens, or DTs. This is extremely dangerous as during this time vital signs, like blood pressure, heart rate and temperature can enter into dangerous ranges and the individual is at risk of dying. Seriously, death. Withdrawal can also lead to seizures, an over activity of the brain, and that itself can also lead to death. Both alcohol intoxication and withdrawal can lead to death. Am I being clear enough? Also, hangovers suck.

Alcohol also causes damage over the long term. A lot of damage. More damage than any other drug and to virtually every body system. It can cause problems in the brain (besides just the addiction) leading to a state of permanent cognitive impairment. It can cause nerve damage and pain, stomach issues, liver issues, kidney issues, and even skin problems. It is linked to cancers found all over the body, and is responsible for a number of malnourished states. Beer contains alcohol. This seems to be a commonly misunderstood point. While liquor contains more actual alcohol per serving and wine does as well, beer is still alcohol. Switching from liquor to beer is like switching from unfiltered to filtered cigarettes. Sure it may take a little longer to die from COPD, but you are going to wheeze and smell bad the whole time either way. So, yeah, beer is still alcohol. It can cause death in both intoxication and withdrawal. And actually because one consumes a lot of fluid when drinking beer there are some medical conditions associated just with beer drinking. But it is legal, so it must be ok, right? I mean legal is equivalent to moral, ethical and healthy, correct? Please drink responsibly.

**BENZODIAZEPINES:**

These motherfuckers are the worst. Benzodiazepines are things like Xanax, Klonopin, Ativan, Valium, Librium, alprazolam, clonazepam, lorazepam, diazepam...all the -pams and -lams and -zams. These drugs are basically freeze dried alcohol. They are usually prescribed for anxiety. They work pretty well for anxiety, as does alcohol. Because they are so chemically structured like alcohol, they cause the exact same problems as alcohol. See the above description of alcohol intoxication and withdrawal and just substitute benzodiazepines in there because it is exactly the same. So much so that using a benzodiazepine to detox someone from alcohol can be super effective...until you have to detox them off of the benzo. The exception to this is the long term damage. Benzos can hurt your liver in large quantities, but they don't do the damage like alcohol does to the other systems of the body.

Anxiety generally won't kill someone. There are other medications for anxiety that won't kill a person either (if taken correctly). Do they work as well? No, but there are no seizures or death associated with them. It is more common for a person to abuse a benzo in conjunction with another drug, like opiates, to enhance the effects of opiates, but certainly there are lots of people out there who will use Xanax before anything else. Also, the sleep medication Ambien (zolpidem) and the muscle relaxer Soma (methocarbamol) fall into this category. They aren't exactly chemically benzos, but they sure act like it.

**OPIATES:**

Ok, this is a broad category. First of all there are opioids and opiates. Classically, the term opiate refers to natural substances that come from opium. Opium itself can be extracted from the opium poppy[29] and contains chemical compounds, including morphine and codeine. Examples of opiates are morphine, heroin and codeine. Opioids are synthetically produced or semi-synthetic versions of opiates. Like oxycodone, hydrocodone, methadone and fentanyl. But nobody cares. They all work the same and the vast majority of people use the terms interchangeably. There are so many brand names and generics of these. Here are a few that fall into one of these categories: morphine, codeine, heroin, fentanyl, carfentanil, oxycodone, Oxycontin, hydrocodone, Vicodin, Norco, Lortab, Percocet, Percodan, Tylenol #3, Darvocet, Dilaudid, hydromorphone, Opana, methadone, buprenorphine, tramadol, Nucynta. Some of these are more potent than others, but they are all opiates and they all work in the same way. Opiates have varying effects from sedation to increased energy. Pain relief, anti-anxiety and anti-depressant effects can be seen as well. We have natural opiates; they are our endorphins. These bad boys allow us to push through that 26th mile of a marathon despite the fatigue of our muscles. They allow us to power through dangerous situations despite pain or injury. They are the reason that when you sprain your ankle, the first five minutes is excruciating, but then the pain becomes dull and more tolerable.

Opiates, the non-natural ones, are very addictive. This is partially because they release a lot of dopamine into the reward center and partially because they produce a physical dependence very quickly. This means that anyone that takes an opiate for five or more days in a row, starts to have a physical withdrawal when they stop taking them. This physical discomfort often leads to people taking opiates for a lot longer than they are generally needed for actual pain. The majority of people, no matter how long they have been taking them, can and do go through the withdrawal at some point and then they are ok. However, those with a previous addiction to other substances or those with the genetic predisposition for

29 Take note, the poppy is a plant. A naturally growing plant

addiction triggered by opiates, are more likely to actually reactivate the addiction in the case of the former or 'trigger' that gene in the latter because of the physical withdrawal. Then it is no longer just a physical problem. While alcohol and benzos can also produce a physical tolerance, it takes longer to do so. This is why we see a far greater number of young people becoming addicted to opiates than we do alcohol. I often say that opiates are like the Maserati we are driving to hell. Alcohol is like the Schwinn bicycle. They are both going to the same place. The former will get us there more quickly, the latter will beat the crap out of our bodies along the way.

Opiate intoxication causes the heart rate and breathing to slow. It causes the pupils to constrict and become pinpoint. It can cause narcosis, or somnolence, or just plain 'nodding off.' It is the decreased breathing, though, that is super problematic. Intoxication will cause a person to become sleepy and unconscious, and then when their respiratory drive slows down, they aren't getting enough oxygen to live. Basically they stop breathing and as it turns out, we need to breathe to live. This is an overdose. If it is not reversed and/or breathing restored, the person will die.

Withdrawal from opioids is not life threatening, but it feels like death. There is nausea, vomiting, diarrhea, sweats, chills, hot and cold flashes, muscle aches, joint pain and restless limbs. It is like the worst flu ever. And because addicts are unable to tolerate any discomfort in general due to the dopamine dysfunction, when they get thrown into a week long episode of the worst discomfort imaginable, there is a tendency for them to say 'fuck this, I can't do it' and they go out and find something. They overestimate their tolerance. And they overdose. And die. Physical withdrawal from opiates does not kill a person, but the process of trying to get through it can lead to behaviors that cause death.

Despite the shit show that opiates are, they actually cause very little damage to the body. Heroin, if contaminated, can certainly lead to kidney problems. IV drug use comes with a whole host of trouble including infections in the veins, skin, and heart as well as transmissible diseases like HIV and Hepatitis. But the drugs themselves are relatively safe in terms of body system damage. That is the nicest thing I will say about them.

## STIMULANTS:

The stimulants includes a number of drugs including methamphetamine, an illicit drug, as well as cocaine, directly from the coca plant.[30] The amphetamines, like adderall and Ritalin (methylphenidate), are generally prescribed for ADD/ADHD. These have a very fast onset, so they are very appealing with the crowd that needs instant gratification. But they wear off quickly too. They are stimulants, so they stimulate. They increase the heart rate, blood pressure and temperature *during* intoxication. They increase energy and endurance, and reduce appetite. So with these drugs, the danger is during active use. They can cause stroke and heart attack among other horrific medical and psychiatric consequences. They can cause death while intoxication is occurring. The withdrawal involves a 'crash' from all that energy but is not dangerous. Don't get me wrong, they feel like shit, but not in a death-is-imminent way.

MDMA, or ecstasy, falls into a few categories but I will include it here. This drug is stimulating, but is not as rapid in onset and can last longer. It produces a great deal of euphoria which can be appealing to someone with a long history of feeling dysthymia or depressed and cause them to repeatedly use it. It also very strongly affects the release of serotonin, which is also a pleasure drug but it is not tied in the same way to the reward system as dopamine is. While it is addictive, it is unusual to see as the presenting 'symptom' when people come to treatment. The prescription drug Provigil also falls into this category. It is used for narcolepsy and for people who do shift work. Used as prescribed, it generally isn't addictive, however, in large amounts it can mimic the effects of cocaine. Long term use of stimulants can lead to enlarged hearts and other damage to the cardiovascular system.

## BARBITURATES:

These are sedatives. Long acting sedatives. They were abused widely in the 60's. Things like seconal, tuonol, barbital. We do see some use of these substances, but they aren't as widely abused. They can cause overdose from sedation and respiratory depression like

30 Also a plant.

opiates. Currently we see butalbital, as part of a migraine medication called Fioricet, and phenobarbital is used for alcohol and benzo withdrawal management and seizure disorders. They can be abused and are very very dangerous if there is a physical dependence and withdrawal. People die from withdrawal.

**INHALANTS:**

Fortunately, these are not as widely abused as many of the other drugs. Unfortunately, they are highly addictive and are one of the few substances that cause permanent damage to the brain (the other being alcohol). Even more unfortunately we see inhalant use most commonly in young people. It is a very rapid high, a rapid peak and a rapid crash. This allows the person to use over and over throughout the day and cause more and more damage. This is what some call 'huffing' and involves inhaling a noxious chemical on purpose. This could be paint, gasoline, air freshener, nitrous oxide or even permanent markers. So basically household items or shit that is easy to steal.

**HALLUCINOGENS:**

This class of drugs includes LSD, psilocybin mushrooms, mescaline and peyote, among others. These work in different areas of the brain and releases dopamine in smaller quantities and generally do not result in addiction. They can result in permanent states of psychosis and/or trigger underlying psychiatric disorders in some instances.[31]

31 There is currently a trend called 'microdosing' where people are using small doses of hallucinogens to treat all different maladies including depression, anxiety, ADHD and general stress among other things. The research is promising but minimal and I have serious doubts that the majority of people who are taking it upon themselves to be pharmacists are doing it correctly. But for our purposes, these drugs, especially in 'microdoses' will have little, if any, effect on addiction either positive or negative.

**ALL OTHER DRUGS:**

There are a whole host of over the counter and prescription medications that fall somewhere on the spectrum of addiction. Kratom, for example, is available at 'head shops' and the internet. It is a plant that is currently being promoted in the underground world of the interwebs as a way to get off of heroin. It works like an opiate. Which means that people abuse it, get addicted to it, and ultimately have withdrawal coming off of it. Cough syrup, dextromethorphan, coricidin, robitussin...when taken in large doses can produce a high and even a hallucinogenic effect. Seroquel, gabapentin, wellbutrin and even phenergan are prescription medications that don't fall into any of the above categories, but that are widely abused. A good litmus test of whether something is addictive is to threaten to take it away. If the person gets very upset and indignant about it, they are probably at least mildly addicted to it. No one has ever had a fit if I stopped their blood pressure or thyroid medication. Ever.

**MARIJUANA:**

Marijuana could probably have a whole book of its own. In fact, I am certain there are thousands of them. Here is my two cents. If you do not have addiction, and you are not taking any other addictive substances and want to use marijuana either recreationally or medicinally, by all means, go ahead. It is certainly less problematic than alcohol recreationally and it is far less problematic than opiates or benzos medicinally. However, due to all the fancy schmancy talk early about dopamine and the reward system, there is a very very high probability that marijuana, specifically the THC component, will both prevent the reward system from healing properly and prevent the cortex from developing other behavioral coping skills. If you need to smoke pot because it's Tuesday and work was a little busy, then what will your brain need to deal with the stress of a house fire or loss of a loved one? So for addicts, I think the risk is too high. If you told me that eating broccoli could potentially cause me to relapse on heroin eventually, I am certain that I would remove broccoli from my diet. Completely. The reward from eating broccoli is not worth the misery of going back to a life a using. If you don't have a problem with a substance, then it should not be a problem not to use it. But, you do you. Unless you are my patient, then do what I say.

## NICOTINE:

Nicotine is another one that needs it's own book. This drug is so complex in how and where it works in the brain that I generally don't include it in my lectures. But I always get asked about it. So, yes, nicotine is addictive. And yes, nicotine does cause the dopamine receptors to down regulate, but to a lesser degree. So smokers do actually have a higher threshold for pleasure, but it is not so high that 'normal' things can't give them joy. Nicotine itself does cause some changes in the body, but most of the negative health effects that are linked with nicotine are also linked with actual tobacco. Tobacco contains tons of gross chemicals and things like tar. It is these things that cause a lot of the damage associated with smoking and chewing tobacco. The nicotine is what keeps a person coming back for more despite the wheezing and frostbite from having to smoke outside. Because the effects seem so minor and drawn out, there is a lack of desperation driving tobacco users to quit. We see the same patterns as with other drugs. We see people try to quit numerous times and fail. We see individuals lying to spouses and parents and hiding their tobacco use. We see people walking two miles in the snow to the convenience store to pick through the giant ashtray to find a butt that someone put out, just for that one hit. We see people buying tobacco with pennies scrounged up from couch cushions.

We do know in the treatment world that if a person quits tobacco at the same time they quit other drugs, their chances of long term success improve significantly. We also know that not allowing people to smoke during treatment for substance use disorder results in a lot of walking out, flipping of the bird and
general 'fuck this place' sentiments.

## CAFFEINE

Caffeine is not addictive. Not in the way I have been talking about. It does have effects similar to a mild stimulant, but the effect peaks at very low levels before it becomes uncomfortable. Ever had too much coffee? You quickly move past 'alert' into jittery and on into 'oh crap, am I having a heart attack.' That's generally not the kind of euphoria one is seeking. It does cause physical dependence though. So you get withdrawal, which include headaches and mild flu like symptoms for a couple of days. It is avoidance of these symptoms more than seeking the stimulation that keeps people driving through Starbucks.

## SUGAR:

I honestly don't even want to start on this topic. It is overwhelming. For now, know that we as a nation consume way too much sugar. It is pumped into all our processed foods because it makes crappy food taste better. It also activates the reward system. This is especially true in high quantities. Which means we buy more and there is nothing more addictive to a corporation than money and power. So they lure us in with more and more sugar. It drains our energy stores, causes obesity and diabetes, creates states of irritability and drives us to seek more of the same. Also, sugar is the actual reason we seek out most of the caffeinated beverages that we do. The fancy coffees at Starbucks, the energy drinks at the convenience store and the old standby of soda, particularly Mountain Dew.[32] These things all contain caffeine, in varying amounts, but what they do have in common is sugar. Lots and lots of sugar.

---

32 Seriously, have you ever seen people that drink Mountain Dew? It is astounding how much of that stuff they will drink. I knew a girl who used to sleep with a 2 liter of it next to her bed.

SIXTEEN:

## ADDICTIONS BEYOND DRUGS

*"So many things are possible*
*so long as you don't know they're impossible."*
– Norton Juster,
The Phantom Tollbooth

When I got clean, and I went through all of my CDs (this was before mp3 or any other significant technology), I was able to tell you all about everyone I ever dated or admired and nothing about myself. My entire self image was constructed of carefully created illusions. If you liked something, I researched it in secret and just waited for my moment to nonchalantly drop a knowledge bomb on the topic so that you would think that I was cool. Cooler than anyone else. If you liked a certain type or look, I subtly and strategically changed my look until I embodied my version of it. I had no idea who I was. My 'me' was entirely dependent on you.

During rehab and the subsequent counseling and self exploration, I did find out a lot about who I am and what I like. Today I wear that proudly. Codependency is addiction. Addiction is chronic and if we aren't careful, if we aren't vigilant, it creeps back in.

My first husband was an amazing guy. We both had a couple of years clean when we met. We were both exploring similar spiritual paths and we had similar interests. So at first, I was very comfortable being me. After a couple of years, and his first of many relapses, a side of my disease crept in and totally blindsided me. While I was able to maintain my tastes in music, clothes, and literature independent of the relationship, the relationship itself began to consume me. I became the textbook spouse of an addict. One who was working a program for my own abstinence from drugs, but nothing else. I was sleeping with the debit card and car keys in the pillowcase. I was so distracted at work, which at the time was my family medicine residency, that I could only think about what I was going to go home to: a missing husband, a passed out husband, a host of missing electronics and jewelry? It was a super fun game and by super fun, I mean a nightmare. We fought a lot. He made a lot of promises. I became an expert on checking phone and bank records, and I made friends with the pawn shop owner. While I could see the dysfunction in my life, I felt powerless to stop it. Because in spite of it all, I loved him. As I continued to work on my spiritual growth, find my purpose in life, the universe did for me what I couldn't do for myself. His shenanigans landed him in jail, circumstances surrounding my moving and his release meant that he couldn't come live with me right away. I thought this was a great opportunity for him to really work on his recovery independent of me. I thought this was a great opportunity for me to see him do that, from a distance, where I had just gotten used to the serenity that had found its way back to my brain space. I told him 'you do you and I'll do me and if we both do it right, we will wind up back together.' Eight months later he overdosed and died. I can't even put into words the grief, the overwhelming heartbreak, that I still feel. But I am certain that if I didn't have that space, that time, to really step back and look at that piece of my addiction, that addiction to love, both of our diseases would've taken us.

There are tons of behavioral, or 'process' addictions. Certainly people have heard of gambling addiction, co-dependency, and sex addiction. People talk about exercise addiction, workaholism and gaming addiction. There is also food addiction and it's sister, over-eating addiction...yup, two different things. There is social media addiction, shoplifting addiction. Many of these are just fodder for memes or punchlines to jokes. Usually, they are kind of funny and kind of true. But when these things are true addictions, they bear some stark similarities both biologically and behaviorally to drug addiction. They also have some characteristics that are unlike drug addiction.

To begin, the process addictions are not 'cross reactive', meaning that if you are addicted to gambling you are not also automatically addicted to sex. This differs from the drugs because the actual addiction to drugs is occurring at the same place with the same neurotransmitters in similar quantities no matter which drug is used. The process addictions have individual effects, independent of each other and unique to different individuals. Those with drug addiction may be at risk for one or more of the process addictions, but it is not always, or even often the case. Those with process addictions, however, are at higher risk for drug addiction at some point.

Anecdotally, I have found that a disproportionate number of gastric bypass or other stomach shrinking procedure patients wind up on detox units. Why? Because for many of them, the reason behind their weight gain was food addiction. And while they are required to get a psychological assessment prior to the surgery, no one bothers to have them seen by an addiction specialist. If the primary problem is addiction to food, or 'coping with food', and we don't address it, then it will just manifest in a different way. Once they can no longer get that dopamine hit from emotional eating, because their stomachs are too small, the brain begins seeking it out in another form. For many, it is when they realize they get a quick and sudden buzz from alcohol due to their disrupted absorption system. For others, the opiate pain pills they got after the surgery make an adequate replacement for the food. Had the issue been dealt with, or at least addressed prior to any surgery we might have been able to prevent so much more damage in the lives of these people and those around them.

Remember that pleasure threshold thing I was talking about earlier? Well in certain individuals, again, mostly genetically predetermined, if they expose their brain to enough certain addictive activity, they create the same sort of change in pleasure threshold. For example if someone with a predisposition for gambling starts to gamble on a regular basis, the act of gambling produces more than a normal amount of dopamine release for that person. So their reward system down regulates the dopamine receptors and their threshold for pleasure moves slightly outside of 'normal'. Which means that gambling is one of the only things that can give that person pleasure. So they continue to do it even when they lose their home, spouse, job, etc. And because it is what they turned to to relieve stress or 'blow off steam', it replaces the other coping skills. When the ability to gamble is taken away, this person may find themselves seeking solace in alcohol or drugs, because they don't even realize what the gambling has done to their brain. And then, well, we have already talked about that.

The behavioral addictions can occur primarily, that is, they can occur first and remain as the only addiction a person every has, or they can occur secondary to substance addiction. Let's pretend we are addicted to substances. We decide to give them up because they have wreaked havoc on our lives and so we go to treatment and we decide to abstain from all substances. Well, the dopamine threshold doesn't just go back to normal after a few days without drugs. In fact, it could take months or years. So during that time that the threshold is moving down, there is a period where all addicts appear depressed. Because we are. It is depressing to not be able to feel normal joy. This depression is different than the clinical, organic depression we see in mental illness. That depression deals more with serotonin and norepinephrine in different areas of the brain. No, this depression is really just a dopamine pure dysthymia and it is expected. It is also the reason that many people want to jump on the bandwagon to assume that all addicts are self medicating their depression. Maybe. In some cases. In many cases, the addiction actually caused the depression, and time away from substances will help, but I digress. So, that threshold is slowly moving down and suddenly we realize that watching porn or going to the gym for four hours makes us feel better. So, we continue to do those things. The movement of the threshold, which is really just the regeneration of dopamine receptors, halts. Now we can only really feel good and normal when we are doing those activities. The problem is that for us, we are doing unhealthy amounts of porn watching or exercising. We are causing problems with our relationships or putting too much strain on our bodies. We are having consequences and we struggle to stop. Finally, though, we decide enough is enough. We haven't had a drink or a drug for eight months, we don't need this porn or exercise problem to be our undoing. So we decide to stop. But we have done NOTHING in that eight months to strengthen our frontal cortex. We have not practiced or worked on any coping skills. So when we stop the behavior, we suddenly launch back in to that depressive state with no way to deal with it. Even though, if we could ride it out, the receptors would eventually come back to normal, we aren't equipped to deal with that. So we reach for a substance. Generally something we view as relatively harmless, like marijuana or beer, which produces a spike in dopamine and starts the reversal of the receptors all over again. And so on and so on.

I have often been asked about a 'lesser of two evils' situation. The question usually comes up, "Is it really so bad that I am addicted to working? I mean I am creating a great financial legacy for my family." To which I query, "Do you mean the family that never sees you because you are working all the time?" Or,"Isn't exercise healthy? Don't you doctors recommend that we exercise?" To which I reply, "Yes, of course. But not to the point of wearing out your kidneys, tearing tendons and causing electrolyte imbalances, causing you to miss days of work and put you at risk of losing your job. None of those things are healthy." Are the process addictions 'lesser' addictions than drugs? In some ways, they do reduce harms. Such as the elimination of intravenous use or the decrease in the number of drunken blackouts and their subsequent legal issues. Over time, these addictions cause their own harm and while that is occurring, they are preventing real healing from happening. Because sometimes these addictions include behaviors that are necessary for normal life functioning, the recovery process is slightly different. For example,food addiction. Recovery from food addiction does not involve starving oneself. It involves identifying specific trigger foods. Foods that trigger an emotional response to over eat or foods that are the 'go to' for self soothing. Those foods are restricted in a recovery program.

In sex addiction, the problem behavior may be sexual interactions outside of a committed relationship (provided that both parties actually committed and agreed upon a monogamous relationship), so that individual would not abstain from sexual encounters with their partner, but only in affairs outside of that relationship.

SEVETEEN:

# THE DISEASE MODEL....
# I DIDN'T FORGET, *YOU* FORGOT

*"Don't judge each day by the harvest you reap,*
*but by the seeds that you plant."*

– Robert Louis Stevenson

I can't tell you the number of times I have heard someone say, "I am so addicted to XYZ" and what they really mean is that they really like XYZ and they have poor self control regarding XYZ. I also often hear, "I have an addictive personality" which isn't really a thing. What they generally mean by that is that they tend to go to extremes or they tend to like things at full force until they become bored with them. A true 'addictive personality,' if there were such a thing, would likely be a personality that was ever changing to suit the needs of the individual and those around them. It would be a personality that was dominated by manipulation, dishonestly, control and deep down self loathing. A personality that makes moving into the world of using substances almost second nature. I don't think that's what you meant when you said, "Oh, I avoid chocolate covered strawberries, I have such an addictive personality I would probably eat the whole box!"

Addiction is a disease process. There are actual changes in the brain that make it next to impossible to stop without help. For it to be an addiction, it needs to produce a negative effect. There needs to be negative consequences that the individual recognizes, acknowledges, and then just plows on through, leaving them with a sense of guilt and shame that triggers the chronic stress cycle.[33]

So it is a disease. Similar to other diseases, it has an organ, a

---

33 Which in turn triggers the dopamine dysregulation, which prompts further use of substances or behaviors, which causes more negative consequences, and so on.

defect in that organ, and symptoms that result because of that defect. The organ involved is the brain. Both the midbrain and the cortex are directly affected. The defect in the midbrain involves a down regulation of dopamine receptors, and in the cortex there is a decrease in activity and a weakening of pathways around stress relief, self soothing and coping skills. The symptoms of the disease include continuing to use the drug or behavior despite knowing better and despite the negative consequences. Craving, the overwhelming sense that we need to change the way we feel and desperately, is another symptom. When cravings occur, we will almost mindlessly reaching for anything we know that will fix that. Symptoms of the disease also include behaving in a way that is contrary to our own value system (hello, guilt and shame), but feeling in the moment that we just have to do it. For those that want to argue that most of the 'symptoms' are behavioral and therefore don't count, please go tell that to the neurosurgeons and psychiatrists that treat frontal lobe syndrome from brain tumors.[34]

---

34 A syndrome of behavioral and personality changes that occur after a trauma to the head

EIGHTEEN:

## IF I BUY INTO THIS DISEASE CONCEPT, WILL YOU TELL ME HOW TO FIX IT?

*"I think I can. I think I can. I think I can. I know I can."*
– Watty Piper,
*The Little Engine that Could*

I was in my third year of medical school, and things were really bad. I was injecting about a gram of heroin a day and trying to maintain some semblance of propriety while rotating at the different hospitals and doctors offices. I was doing a piss poor job. I was sloppy, dirty, unfocused. I can't remember a thing I learned, but I remember giving sob stories to anyone who would listen to get $10 here and $5 there. I remember doing things in dark alleys, public restrooms and parking lots that respectable people don't do. I remember my boyfriend and I laid out a plan to taper down. We had it actually written out, but before the first day was through, we had already blown it. We didn't even have enough for the next day. So I was in the family practice office where I was rotating, completely unfocused, dope sick and miserable. I would be ducking into corners every five minutes to text my boyfriend to see if he had figured anything out. When someone, maybe one of the doctors, approached me and asked if I was ok, I was so on edge I couldn't even come up with anything better than to say that I was having a panic attack. This particular office happened to have a staff psychologist, which I don't think I have seen before or since. This person, whomever it was, brought me in to see the psychologist, explained I was having a panic attack and left me in her office. She was very kind, and if I could remember her name, I would name a wing of my future treatment center after her. She started asking me the gentle, appropriate questions about what was going on at home and what had me so stressed out. My classy ass just burst into tears, pulled up the sleeves of my sweater and showed her my arms. If it were a movie, this would be the scene after which there would be a montage of my recovery. It wasn't a movie. There are a lot of details and most are foggy to me now, but ultimately that kind woman put me in touch with an organization for doctors with substance use disorder. I wasn't quite a doctor yet, but they were willing to help anyway. It sounds nice now and in retrospect, I am extremely grateful. At the time, though, I truly became panicked. What had I done?? I told my secret. People knew. I was going to have to actually jump through some hoops. I immediately set to work trying to figure out how to get these people to agree to my terms. I was absolutely not doing group or inpatient treatment. I was not going to tell my school or my family. I was just going to quietly and secretly get well and no one would be the wiser.

Hear me when I say that I was absolutely resolute on these points. I refused to believe that it would have to be any other way. If these people would have 'met me where I was at,' I would currently be dead. Not writing a book. Dead. Incidentally, after much cajoling, pleading and begging, I wound up going into residential treatment for 72 days, followed by group and individual counseling for a year. Two weeks prior to going into residential, I told my family and my school. So yeah, I showed them.

Those 72 days of my life were absolutely life changing. I did not just get freedom from substances, I got freedom from self hatred. Freedom from bondage to illusion. Freedom from myself. All the while, as these patient and dedicated staff members were giving me these gifts, I was still walking around thinking I did not belong there. I was different. I could do this. It was only after daily structure, being called on my bullshit, being forced to follow 'stupid rules' and do 'stupid assignments' that the real me, the previously unseen me, emerged. One of the ladies at the rehab told me after my first thirty days that I reminded her of a flower that had burst into bloom. It was corny, but it was how I felt. There was *nothing* about the treatment options that I was given that appealed to me in any way. If the threat of being kicked out of medical school with an already enormous debt load and no sustainable way to repay it wasn't looming over me, I would never have agreed. But the universe really does unfold like that, doesn't it? Just people and circumstances in certain places at just the right time to coax your life in the direction it needs to go.

In behavioral health, there is a need to 'meet people where they are.' This sets individuals up for very specific treatment plans that are tailored to their personality and mental health needs, but also to work within their desires. This becomes a sticky wicket in substance use disorder because most often the addict does not want what they actually need, or what would benefit them most. This is why treatment for addicts often looks like a cookie cutter treatment plan, but it is just that the disease is so predictable that most people need similar skills and structure.

NINETEEN:

## BUT FIRST, DO NO HARM....
## NO, WAIT: FIRST, REDUCE HARM

*"Fall seven times, stand up eight."*

-Japanese proverb

Before someone commits to 'do whatever it takes,' there is a period of time where they know that there is a problem, but they just want to reduce the amount of consequences they are facing, not necessarily stop. Harm reduction has many different facets, and it is the one place in the treatment of chronic disease processes that we really do have to meet people where they are.

Some elements of harm reduction include non abstinence based medication, such as older methadone clinics and marijuana maintenance programs (either physician sanctioned or self imposed). These allow people to stop engaging in harmful behaviors specific to their drug of choice. For example, if a person stops using IV heroin and instead uses methadone (NOT MAT) or marijuana, they reduce the risk of IV transmissable diseases like hepatitis and HIV. If they are obtaining the methadone and/or marijuana legally, they are reducing harm in that they are not putting themselves at risk by engaging with drug dealers or solicitation of sex for drugs.

Needle exchange sites allow drug users to cut down on the transmissible diseases as well, but also decrease the risk of endocarditis, an infection of the valves of the heart that comes most often from the use of dirty needles. New needles also cut down on the risk of skin infections and vascular disruptions (blow or 'junked' veins) because they are sharp and don't require the same force to puncture skin and veins.

Safe injection sites allow addicts to go somewhere besides the backseat of their car under a bypass at 3am to use their drugs.

There are usually trained professionals that can assist if an overdose occurs. Safe injection sites are illegal in the US, but exist under the radar and honestly, they have shown *huge* promise in decreasing the number of overdose deaths.

Narcan distribution has also shown to decrease the number of deaths related to opioid overdose. Narcan is an opioid reversal agent and if administered relatively quickly after overdose, it can revive a person long enough to get them to medical professionals for further stabilization. It is similar to the cardioversion (AED) units that people use when someone is having a heart attack. It does not treat the disease, just reverses death. Organizations like project DAWN (Death Avoided With Narcan) have provided this medication for free to addicts and family members and community organizations.

TWENTY:

# IT ALL BEGINS WITH DETOX

*"There is no living thing that is not afraid when it faces danger. True courage is in facing danger when you are afraid."*

– L. Frank Baum,
*The Wizard of Oz*

Actually, it all begins with a decision. A decision that you are worth the discomfort. That you are worth the hard work. That you are worth the unfamiliar, the frightening, the raw and honest truth. And you are worth it. But after that decision, detox. I have already discussed all of the drugs, so I won't go over that again. Basically the gist of detox is to safely get the crap out of your system so you can move on to the next phase of treatment. Detox is not treatment. Let me rephrase that in an understandable way, ***Detox is not treatment***. Detox is just that, detoxification. It is a medical stabilization. It is a way to safely taper down or replace the substance of choice so that the addict doesn't, you know, die. Most detox facilities will only take those who need to come off of alcohol, benzos and opiates. The stimulants, while still a shitty 'detox', do not entail a dangerous withdrawal, at least not medically, so most insurances won't cover that kind of detox. Once the substances are at least at a safe level in the system, the ***actual*** treatment for the addiction can commence.

TWENTY-ONE:

# QUIET THE MIDBRAIN

*"Happiness is the only good. The time to be happy is now.*
*The place to be happy is here.*
*The way to be happy is to make others so"*

- Robert Green Ingersoll

The first goal is really to try to get the midbrain under some kind of control. That tiger is angry and very distracting. The cravings come hard. The anxiety is overwhelming. In general, we start the process of quieting the midbrain in one of two ways. The first, is abstinence from all addictive drugs. Many of the harm reductionists or moderationists will argue that replacing the drug of choice with a 'less harmful' substance is appropriate. For most true addicts, this proves to be a waste of time, as does moderation. And most true addicts give this a whirl first because it is certainly the most appealing. Hey, smokers, have you ever tried 'cutting down' and then just staying at that lesser amount? Or have you ever tried quitting by switching brands of cigarettes? The cliched expression that many people use here is the 'changing seats on the Titanic,' reference. Sadly, this is truer than not. Remember that all addictive drugs release these massive spikes of dopamine? Well, in what way does it make sense that the brain will stop craving massive spikes of dopamine by giving it massive spikes of dopamine? I totally understand that the conscious *experience* of using one substance to another differs, but subconsciously, where the addiction occurs, *there is no difference*. So pick your poison. If the 'not as great' effects of using a different drug are worth the risk of potentially going back to your drug of choice, then go for it. For me, personally, they are not. Professionally, it seems irresponsible to promote it. If I had a diabetic who wanted to try only eating sugar in the form of cookies, but would refuse any and all other types of sugar, I would probably not feel comfortable nor equipped to properly treat them. So generally, I promote abstinence or, the other tool for quieting the midbrain, Medication Assisted Treatment (MAT).

Now, before you blow your stack with your soapbox opinions of MAT, hear me out. First of all, if drugs work in the midbrain, then so do medications. Now, I will never stand in front of a crowd, or write down for all to read that a 'drug is the cure for drug addiction.' I just don't believe that, and if it were true, then there would be one medication to rule them all. The Precious. That is to say that there would be one medication that provides a steady state of dopamine and relieves withdrawal and cravings no matter what the original drug of choice was. There is no such medication. There are medications, though, that have been shown to help with cravings for alcohol use and cravings and withdrawal in opioid use. These medications are tools that I use in conjunction with the other stuff I will talk about.

Here are the following arguments I hear most frequently against MAT:

You are just replacing one drug with another.

Yes. I am replacing one very harmful and illegally obtained drug that has a rapid tolerance rate with a legal, long acting, minimal tolerance rate version that I can control. I am reducing the amount of harm and consequences going on in the addict's life so that they are able to start becoming a productive member of society and have enough focus to start working on the who and why of their addiction.

It is just a crutch.

You bet. If I break my leg, someone better give me a crutch to take the pressure off of the broken bone so that it can heal. Most of the time, with physical therapy, following medical instructions, home exercise and time, people are able to get off the crutches. Sometimes, the break is so bad, they need crutches or a wheelchair for life.

It is still mood and mind altering:
(buprenorphine and methadone).

Only the first couple of days or if it is being abused. And if it is being abused it is at least in part because the provider is not providing any of the other actual treatment necessary.

It is a cop out.

How so? It is only a tool to fight against the use of one specific drug. Addiction has little to do with one specific drug.[35] So while buprenorphine or naltrexone might help someone not use opioids, it is doing nothing to prevent them from using meth or xanax. Nope, they have to actually do the work to be able to stay away from those things. They are not copping out of anything. They are getting the relief from the overwhelming cravings for one drug, not from the cravings to escape.

Arguments *in favor* of MAT as monotherapy:

The studies show that MAT alone is as effective as MAT with counseling.

Yes, it is. At keeping people off the one drug they were using. Not my goal. Survival is great, but my goal is to help addicts optimize their lives. That can't be done with MAT alone. I am not saying that every addict wants or should want more than to 'just stop using one drug,' and if that is the case, there are plenty of physicians out there willing to provide only MAT. Usually for cash.[36] Many of them will even provide a higher dose than is medically necessary so that the patient can sell the excess as a means to pay for the expensive visits. Sort of like a pimp or a kingpin. They're out there and there are more of them than there are of me. Don't worry if that makes you anxious, most of these folks will also provide a prescription for a benzo too. And some adderall if that xanax makes you too sleepy. Healthcare

35 Please see previous chapters if you don't understand this.

36 There are a few good addiction doctors out there that have to charge cash because their own history of addiction put them in a position that third party payors will not contract with them. They generally charge more reasonable cash prices and they usually have a relationship with a treatment center where they refer patients for the therapy portions of treatment.

at its finest. Definitely the sort of physician whose treatment plan is bound to be successful...Oh no, wait, I meant the sort of physician who is bound to lose their license. Tomato, tomahto.

Patients are uncomfortable with all of the treatment requirements or they have to work/provide for their family and can't find the time to go to counseling, groups, meetings.

OK. I will be here when they lose all of that because they didn't do those things and then relapsed. Newsflash, addicts are uncomfortable with everything except a drug. They are lacking dopamine receptors. Dopamine is the comfort chemical in addition to the pleasure chemical. Did I forget to mention that earlier? Sorry about that. But even addiction aside, how many memes are out there that talk about how growth can only occur when you step outside your comfort zone, or some such blather. And memes are life, amIright? I mean, comfort really shouldn't be a driving force when your life is on the line, should it? Especially when the comfort zone appears to lie somewhere between a crack house and a courthouse.

For most addicts that I treat, their families and jobs did not take priority over using. Recovery from addiction does allow individuals to work and repair relationships, but the treatment part needs to take priority. Otherwise, how do they deal with a jerk of a boss or a nagging spouse?

People always want to know, if we quiet the midbrain either by medication or by abstinence, does the pleasure threshold come back to normal? The answer is yes, it does. However, it is a 'friable' system, meaning that once it is broken it will default back to broken with minimal provocation. If someone's genes dictated that it would take 1000 uses of a substance for the addiction to occur, for the dopamine receptors to start down-regulating, they may use substances for a while before this change occurs. However, once it occurs, even after the threshold goes back to normal, it only take one use to start the process of receptor down regulation again. Left alone, this process of repopulating the midbrain could take up to two full years. However, working on the cortex and spiritual skills can significantly speed this process up. And that is what we want, because remember, the entire time that the reward system is re-regulating, the individual is feeling miserable and 'deaf' to pleasure. So the quicker the better. There are few things that set a person up for failure quicker than extreme discomfort coupled with an inability to deal with discomfort. Add to that zero patience and a brain screaming at them that they are *entitled to feel better* and we see the dismal recovery rates that we see.

TWENTY-TWO:

## BUILDING UP THE CORTEX

*"We can complain because rose bushes have thorns,
or rejoice because thorn bushes have roses."*
– Abraham Lincoln

This is it, kids. This is the part in Scooby Doo where we pull off the mask of the monster to reveal the true villain. The cortex. The prefrontal cortex mostly, but some other cortex-y places as well. The frontal cortex of humans is vastly complex. There is so much going on and so little we understand. A pure reductionist believes that the very thoughts and emotions you have reading this sentence are nothing more than complex chemical and electrical interactions in the brain. Spiritualists believe that it is the universe, God or some other unearthly force that gives rise to the chemical and electrical interactions we see in the brain. Most people fall somewhere in between.

Regardless of your beliefs, there is no question that our logic, judgment, impulsivity, self control and skills arise, in part at least, to activity in the cortex. When a person is using drugs (or behaviors) compulsively, they are essentially using them as their coping mechanism. See, the drugs are never the problem, the drugs are the solution, to a weakened ability to cope. Whether it was never a strong skill pathway to begin with or it weakened over time from disuse, matters little. Because now the task is to build this pathway (back) up. Here is the kicker. It kind of sucks. Even if we become super skilled at coping and stress relief, it never feels as good as the drugs did. It also doesn't cause nearly the problems. There is some degree of sacrifice that has to occur in the initial stages of recovery. There is some degree of boredom that has to occur, some lack of drama that makes an addict feel restless. Many believers in harm reduction or moderation don't feel that this is necessary. Mostly because they want to continue to chemically escape as much as possible without the consequences. Sometimes it is just because it is painful to think that we should ever have to be uncomfortable or actually wait for anything. Ever. We will promote hard work to achieve life goals, but not to achieve recovery from addiction. I am not saying it has to be a horrible, painful drawn out experience, but compared to the instant gratification of active use, it kind of seems that way.

So how do we do this boring, anxiety provoking work? With the help of others. I am not kidding. If you are an addict, please, please, please stop trying to do it yourself. You mostly suck at your own life right now. Seriously, your very best work, the best decisions you have made in the past years, months, weeks, days have brought you here. Reading this book. This book was your best decision of the day. So you see? Your decision making ability basically blows.

So, who do you ask for help? Mom? Dad? Uncle Joe? Um, no. I am assuming all those people have been resources for you all along. Yet here we are. If your friends and family are 'sober' and supportive, that is phenomenal. Seriously, I am so happy for you. Definitely put that in the win column. But it is not enough. You really need the help from someone who has been where you are and got better. Someone who also sucked at life and now sucks at it way less, because someone helped them. Before you jump on that fur lined pity pot because I told you that you suck at your life, let me tell you something else. You are an amazing resource for someone else. Yep. The yin and the yang of the whole thing is that the more you are terrible at YOU, the better you are at seeing, pointing out and correctly guiding OTHERS. Can you see how professionals in this field (at least the ones that actually get it) would be promoting things like group therapy and self help groups and meetings? Because your insight into other people is an invaluable resource to those people. However, they are the only ones that can help you tap into your own potential because your life will not get much better without them. It a vicious, positive circle of happiness and annoying-ness.

So, while you are figuring out how to ask advice from and take direction from, essentially, strangers, how do we deal with this boredom? We have to fill our lives with something good, to replace the chaos, drama and drug taking. Now I know what you're thinking. "Whoa, there. You just told us a few chapters back that filling our day with exercise, porn and food could be almost as bad as drugs." Yes, I did, young padawan. Thank you for listening. So no, we are not going to fill our days with slightly less but also problematic behaviors. We are going to fill it with purpose.

One of *the* most common complaints I get about twelve step programs is the use of the word and reference to 'God'. No matter how many times I try to explain to people that this is merely a semantics issue, most people either don't know what semantics means or they are unable to untie their own old belief system from the new one being presented. If you read through the twelve steps, or any other document meant to promote spiritual growth, I urge you to replace the word 'God' with 'Purpose.' Go ahead. Go read the Big Book of Alcoholics Anonymous or the Basic Text of Narcotics Anonymous, or whatever dogmatic best seller is popular right now. Replace all the 'God', 'higher power', 'Lord' or whatever with 'purpose.' I'll wait...

Anyone can stop using drugs for a period of time. Even for a couple of years. But it requires a purpose in life to maintain abstinence. Quite frankly, if you find true purpose for your life, the moderation equation becomes moot, because you have no desire to chemically erase any part of your purpose driven life.

Before we get to purpose, let's go back to that cortex strengthening. The brain is not a muscle, but let's pretend it acts like one. Let's pretend it acts like our upper arm. It is composed of the bicep and the tricep (among others). These are opposing muscles. The bicep helps bend the arm at the elbow and the tricep helps extend or straighten the arm at the elbow. Imagine if we went to the gym and we only exercised the bicep. It would get very strong. But because we are ignoring the tricep, our arm would eventually start to bend and we would be unable to fully straighten it from the force of the bicep and the lack of force from the tricep. So we need to balance the arm workout so that we are strengthening both muscle groups equally. Now, let's imagine that our skill pathways in the cortex are like the tricep and our reward system is like the bicep. When we are using drugs, we are doing every bicep curl imaginable. We are hammer curling fools, but we are totally neglecting our triceps. Because when we look in the mirror, all we see is the bicep.
(Gun show, anyone?)

We need to first lay off the bicep work for a period of time and allow the muscle to weaken a bit. That is, allow the reward system to re-calibrate back to its normal dopamine threshold. Which we have already established can only be done with abstinence over time or with MAT. While this is happening, we need to start doing some tricep dips and skull crushers (or whatever they're called). At first, we really need to put a lot of effort into this tricep work. Almost as much work as we had been putting into the biceps before. The harder we work on the tricep up front, the more quickly the balance between the two muscles occurs. Similarly, the harder we work at putting our recovery into action, the quicker we start to feel better. This is why most treatment centers have really intensive recommendations. Including inpatient treatment, partial hospitalization, intensive outpatient...plus individual counseling...plus self help groups and development of social supports. WTF. So. Much. Work.

Because we know that if you go to an occasional meeting, meet with a counselor once a month and maybe get to a couple of groups, you are basically doing one tricep dip every couple of days. The likelihood that the bicep will remain stronger is high.

If I take my car to the auto mechanic because I am feeling a vibration and hear a slight squeaking when I brake, he will likely tell me that my brake pads need to be replaced as soon as possible. Now I say, "I've been driving this car for 10 years. I know it better than anyone. I don't want to pay the money or take the time to do that," and I leave. I go home and put air in my tires instead. Then I am out on the highway and my brakes start squealing and grinding and I end up causing an accident, who is the idiot? The expert that advised me of the problem and necessary repair? Or me? The driver that thinks she knows her car best (but who also rides her brakes hard and precipitated the need for new brake pads earlier than the manufacturer recommended)? Treatment providers make recommendations based on the individual and what would work best for them, at least the good ones do. Tired of the analogies? Then just do what is suggested. Stop making excuses. If work and family were not enough to keep you from using before, they aren't enough to keep you from using now.

TWENTY - THREE:

# THE CORTEX GOES TO THE GYM

*"The little grey cells, my friend,*
*the little grey cells! They told me."*

- Agatha Christie,
*The Murder on the Links*

We can focus on one of two areas and preferably a combination of both to successfully provide the cortex a stable workout foundation. We can focus on traditional cognitive skill sets and we can focus on purpose driven, or spiritual skill sets. If you read 'religion' in that last sentence, please go back and read the section on the *spiritual* part of the brain on page 39.

## Cognitive skill sets

Traditional skill sets are things like coping skills as well as learning how to deal with stressors as they come. These can be practical skills, like talking to someone about what is going on, making a 'pros' and 'cons' lists, or journaling. These can also be more abstract skills like breathing techniques, acknowledging and feeling emotions as they pass through you, and grounding. These skill sets also involve some internal reflection and examination of things like triggers, resentments, and fears. Counselors that are well versed in substance use disorder usually have a number of thought provoking exercises and discussion starters to use in both group and individual settings to help the individual learn these things.

I remember my first few sessions with an individual counselor. I spent a lot of time thinking about what would be the right thing to say to make them think that I was highly evolved and further along in the process than most. I was actually neither of those things, but I wanted her to think I was. It was part of my larger scheme to fool the entire treatment facility into thinking I was a star pupil while I was, in fact, not getting any better at all. Admittedly, not one of my finest plans. Fortunately, she was clever. It was harder for me to do this in the group setting though because there were people in the group that were, in fact, more highly evolved and further along in the process than I was. They were quick to point out when I was full of shit. Which was often. In the beginning, this gave me the perfect opportunity to dramatize my victimhood. *How DARE you point out my carefully constructed lies and self destruction!* But over time, as I started to get better and less full of shit, I started to see the other people's lies and self delusion. It became my responsibility to point it out to them because that is what moved me toward healing. Even though in general I am kind of a bitch, it was still uncomfortable to call people out. But since it was what I needed, I had to believe it was what they needed too.

The structure in the residential facility was actually really important too, although, at the time it just seemed gimmicky to me. The fact is that regardless of my school and rotations, my life was so unstructured. If we were going to take out the drugs and the finding of drugs and the finding of money to get drugs and the lying to my family and constructing a double life, then we had to replace it with something. That is easy to do in theory, like, oh yeah, I will start cross stitching and coloring and eat three times a day. Reality, though, doesn't seem to work like that. You don't have to be an addict to know that on a rainy Saturday it is possible to spend the entire day in your jammies binge watching Netflix and eating yourself into oblivion in order to forget the monster to do list that you constructed all week. For most, this idle time may simply result in a longer to do list the next day or a few extra pounds. For addicts, this idle time results in the mental masturbation about just using 'one time' and how that won't be a big deal.

Having a routine is helpful. It is also a really useful tool for knowing when things are slipping. A relapse does not happen with the actual use of a substance, it happens way before that. It starts with the subconscious idea that it would be ok to slack on some things or re-start doing others. Then the behaviors that were keeping us in check start to slip because we no longer have the internal drive to keep them on board. We basically went from red light to green and we just need to get rid of all of our accountability so that we can GO.

If I am late for an appointment because I overslept, one of two things will happen and each is telling about my current state of recovery. The first is that I tell the person I am meeting that I overslept, apologize, thank them for waiting, accept any consequences for my actions and move on.

The second is that after I park my car, but before going in to the appointment, I wipe my hands on my car tires and then wipe them on my shirt. I do my best to appear harried as I rush into the appointment and I explain, apologetically and profusely, that I had a flat tire and had to change it, explaining my tardiness in a 'faultless' narrative.

Guess which one is more comfortable for me. Yeah, the second one. Dishonesty is still my default. The desire to control that person's perception of me is still strong. However, I know that if I tell the lie, I will feel guilty about lying. I will also have to catalogue that lie somewhere in my memory for the next time I run into that person. Then, I have to do a mental checklist of every mutual acquaintance we have in case the story comes up, because I need to be consistent. It just becomes a snowball of fuckery that I am perpetually chasing. If I tell enough lies to enough people, I stop talking to those closest to me because they will see through me. I stop going to places like twelve step meetings or church (if that is your thing) where I will be reminded of my dishonesty. I stop going to my cross stitch group (jk. I don't know if this is a thing.[37]) Basically I start isolating. When I am isolating, I start stewing. I become idle. I mentally perseverate about 'relaxing'.

I decide to drink a glass of wine while I take a nice bubble bath. I've earned it, dammit. I have that glass of wine and 'relax' and nothing bad happens, but I can't tell anyone I had a glass of wine. So I isolate more, because now I would have to lie and even though I would prefer to lie, the guilt and keeping up with the lies is wearing me down. Best to just avoid. A month later, I decide to

---

37 I am told there is a knitting group called Stitch and Bitch and Crochet groups called the Happy Hookers, so there is a high likelihood that there is a cross stitch group and an even higher likelihood that they have a clever, albeit slightly obnoxious, name.

have another glass of wine with my bath. I mean, shit, alcohol wasn't even my drug of choice and I drank a month ago and was fine. Again, this time, all is well. And another month goes by and another glass. Then two weeks. Then I am drinking wine every Friday night with my bath. Then I decide to take a bubble bath every Saturday night too. Now I am drinking a glass (or three) every Friday and Saturday night for six months. I start thinking about my friend that I used to go to the bar with. I am pretty lonely since I have stopped talking to all my sober supports. So I call her. She invites me out. I go. I get shitfaced. Some girl in the bathroom has some cocaine. I do a bump with her. I drink more. I black out. I start asking around for oxycodone. Someone finds me heroin. My relapse didn't start with that heroin. Or with the wine. It started with the lie about why I was late. There were plenty of places along the way that I could've been honest and stopped the relapse process. But I didn't. At least not in this scenario. Which is fiction, but based on real life encounters with actual sober people.

When I am in a good place mentally and spiritually, I behave in a manner consistent with the truth. And I only take bubble baths *sans* wine.

Recognizing all of this, acknowledging this, and having a plan of action for this is all part of the recovery process. The greatest part about creating a social circle of other addicts is that you get to learn all of this from them if you really listen. As an addict, it is always my desire to prove that I am special and unique and that just because you got burnt by the stove doesn't mean I will. So I make the same mistakes you did and suffer the same burns. In recovery, I can listen to someone's story about being burned and make the choice to ***not*** try it. Even if deep down I believe I am immune to heat. I get to spend my time learning my own lessons because I was able to learn from yours. When great scientists discover great things, it is not because they went back and tried to recreate fire, it is because they trusted the work of their predecessors and built upon that. We have the opportunity to stand on the shoulders of giants and get a stellar view of the paths ahead of us. Or we can stay on the ground and keep tripping over the same rocks and sticks as the person in front of us. And you thought it was just about drugs.

**Spiritual skill sets**

The spiritual skill set is not entirely disconnected from the above, but it is achieved in slightly different ways. It requires a lot of internal reflection and a lot of action to change. It can be done in traditional ways, through a church or religion if that appeals to someone. This does not mean that attending mass on Sundays and donating cookies to the bake sale is 'getting spiritual.' It isn't. At all. Spirituality for those that tie it to religion has more to do with the actual personal relationship with God or their Supreme Being, whatever that is. In some ways, I think it is harder to develop spiritually this way because most religions 'allow' a passive approach, a 'just show up and be absolved' system. Spiritual growth takes active work. It can be achieved by doing some sort of meditative journey. Maybe go to Tibet for a year. Stay at a monastery. Study with the tai chi masters. There are lots of ways to do it. The goal is to buildup spiritual assets, one by one, until you are no longer the center of the universe. There is no way to read enough books, listen to enough podcasts or watch enough videos to Youtube your way into spirituality. There is also no right way, other than to say it is unwise to do it alone. A broken brain will not likely choose the best course of action. A broken brain will likely misinterpret lessons along the way. A broken brain cannot fix itself without guidance. But in good company, there is not really a wrong way to do it, it is definitely the personal part of the journey. There are some ways that work best, when followed correctly.

Consider baking a cake. You may watch a bunch of cooking shows or read books where people are baking. So you know that you need flour, sugar, eggs and maybe some other stuff. You need measuring cups and mixing bowls. But if you were to try to figure out quantities and ratios all on your own, you would probably fail. Not just a Pinterest fail, but an edible fail. So you need a recipe. Step by step instructions that tell you exactly how much of what to add and when. Now imagine that you also had a famous baker standing next to you, explaining about sifting and leveling cups of flour. You would probably bake a phenomenal cake. For me, I found a recipe for spirituality, I learned to find the highest quality ingredients, and I surrounded myself with world class bakers.

Here is how I did it:

**I learned the spiritual principle of acceptance.**

Acceptance is so fucking important that I cannot even stress enough the necessity of it in life. I used to walk around with these unconscious expectations for everything. For how this day should go, for how I should look, for how you should look, for how someone should respond. So many shoulds. When life would not match up to those expectations, I would spiral into resentment and manipulation to try to force it. This resulted in a near permanent state of frustration, blaming and playing victim. It also allowed for a lot of drama and chaos. In the beginning of my recovery, people would say "you don't have to like it, but you have to accept it." For me, this is not possible. I cannot reconcile placing a judgment "don't like" with an objective state. Acceptance is the neutralization of a perceived event. The super annoying and overused phrase "it is what it is," is, unfortunately, true. Whatever occurs is what was supposed to occur because it occurred. There is no intrinsic good or bad attached to it. *I* attach the judgment and if I do that, I cannot accept it. So when they said I had to accept that drugs were a problem, that I was out of control and my life was headed toward a dumpster fire, I struggled. Because those were all negative things to me and there was no way I could have a problem. I mean, look how much I had achieved! People with drug problems did not get accepted to medical school and pass boards and make it through the first two years. Objectively, though, I had tried to stop and was unsuccessful. That ***is*** a problem. Being out of control was like my worst nightmare. All of my lies and manipulation were *about* control. I needed to be in control of everything. Objectively, things were happening that I did not intend or orchestrate and I could not make it different from what it was. I was violating my core values without even wanting to. That is a loss of control. My life was headed toward oblivion. Objectively, my life was headed in a direction that I never intended despite my best efforts. So acceptance, for me, is erasing the judgment, observing the facts and acknowledging that it is what it is. There was no fucking way that I was going to learn this on my own. None. It was so contrary to the constant emotional turmoil in which I existed. But one day, I was blessed enough to hear someone else describe it this way. That was the day that I was meant to hear it, because it suddenly and blindingly made sense. I started practicing it every day. Whenever something would cause my temper or sense of injustice to flare up, I would stop and observe, neutralize, and review it objectively. Holy serenity, Batman. I felt like the eye of a storm.

Today, my husband does not put dishes in the dishwasher. He puts them next to, around and on top of the dishwasher. I can't stand dishes lying around. My expectations are that if I explain to him lovingly that it bothers me, he would do me the solid of complying with my request. The reality is that objectively, my husband is not bothered by dishes lying around and unless in that specific moment he is thinking about me and my feelings (instead of the four hundred other things on his to do list), he is not going to remember to put the dishes in the dishwasher. Because it just doesn't register on his radar of annoyances. I accept that he isn't bothered by it. I accept that I am. I accept that as the person bothered by it, I will be the one 'fixing' it most of the time. With acceptance, I just do it. There is no swearing under my breath, holding resentments or getting frustrated over and over. The same holds true on the flip side. Things that I do that bother him and not me will not likely register on my radar most of the time. I am not going to beat myself up for not *making* myself frustrated by something that is not frustrating to me. Things are as they are. That's it.

**I learned the spiritual principle of hope**

Once I accepted that my life was, indeed, objectively more disorganized and unstructured than I had previously been deluding myself into believing, I was disheartened. Because, honestly, what was I supposed to do? If I was 'out of control', then wasn't I 'out of control'? So, I either had to believe that it was possible to get my life back on track or that I was doomed. I had, at least in passing, heard of other people getting their lives together after active addiction. So it was possible, right? I just had to figure out how. I was the one that seemed to be powerless in the situation, having tried multiple times and failing. So who, then? Someone told me to ask around. Find those people who had succeeded. Ask them what they did. I developed hope that whatever worked for them could maybe work for me.

**I learned the spiritual principle of faith**

I grew up in the Catholic faith. I went to Catholic school (Hello? Talk about trauma). My parents were the go-to-church-on-Sundays-and-holidays kind of Catholics. I received the sacraments up to Confirmation. I had only one concept of "God" and faith was tied to that. My mother remarried an agnostic, who I thought was the smartest man alive, until I was about fifteen. He told me that religion was invented by man to tame the masses. He preached that religion was created to help develop civility where there was none. That it was all mumbo jumbo nonsense. He believed in science. What you could see and prove. There was no need to 'believe' anything if you could put your trust in the provable. So I, too, became agnostic and spouted his wisdom as my own. Fast forward about ten years and I am being faced with this dilemma. I have to look at someone else's life and believe that my life could be the same. Not only that, but I had to take that hope and turn it into action. I had to look at what they had done, piece by piece, action by action and apply it painstakingly to my own life. No matter how uncomfortable or awkward it was. And with no more proof that it would work than my faith that it would. I began to see some changes in my thinking, my interactions with others, and my life. I had faith that if I learned acceptance, I would become less angry, impulsive and argumentative. I had faith that if I took certain actions, even if they seemed irrelevant, that I would see changes. With every action I took and every change I saw, I became more courageous and willing to do more. I began to understand that I did not even have to know when to accept and when to act, because I surrounded myself with people who showed me or told me when. I had developed faith in other people and their ability to help me.

**I learned the spiritual principle of honesty**

I talked about dishonesty already and how it was my default. But where I learned how to change that was at a kitchen table with another addict who was nothing like me and exactly like me. She was a single mom, a nurse and an addict whose drug of choice had been alcohol. She had the best laugh I had ever heard in my life. The contagious kind of laugh. Damn near jolly. I met her because I heard her talk about an experience she recently had which I will paraphrase here because it was a long time ago. She said *I was at the laundromat with my boyfriend and I was getting ready to leave and I couldn't find my purse. So I started the usual, beating myself up for being so irresponsible, berating myself for not keeping a closer eye on it, dreading having to call my dad and tell him I needed him to come and get me because, shit, my car keys were in the purse. Just as I was getting ready to call my dad, I looked over and my boyfriend was laughing. He had taken my purse and hid it as a joke. Now, I think it was a stupid joke, but he just wanted to mess with me. At first I started to get really mad and was about to yell at him. Then I stopped and I said, you know, I know you were just playing around, but you have no idea how much that fucked with me. I immediately went to that place of self hatred and self derision. I thought once I again I had fucked up. But I didn't.*

Then she said *I was really proud of myself. Because I realized what I had done. Because I was honest with him about it. Because it didn't turn into a huge argument that it otherwise would have.*

I had never heard someone talk like that. I had never seen someone be so honest with themself, so introspective about something so incredibly stupid. So I asked her to tell me how she did that. We spent a lot of time together talking about it. And once I started talking and writing about things in this honest way, it started to pour out of me. We first only talked about weird things. Like the fact that we would buy a bunch of produce at the grocery store because we wanted to be healthy, but then we would never eat it because we were afraid that if we ate it now, we wouldn't have anymore later if we wanted it and it wound up going bad every time. This was the first time I was giving an honest voice to things that would go on internally. I know it sounds silly now, but at the time it was really a significant turning point. Because in learning to be honest with myself and someone else, I also developed trust and integrity. Trust because she never judged me for the dumb-ass things I said and integrity because she believed that I would tell her the truth. Even if it was uncomfortable. I did not want to violate that trust, I wanted to be trustworthy.

**I learned the spiritual principle of courage**

As I was developing the principles of honesty, trust, and integrity I was doing some work on myself. I had to really start taking a long hard look at the chips on both shoulders, the anger, fear, and resentment that I was holding on to. I had to sit down and really examine why, when people brought up resentments, I still thought about the girl that wrote nasty things about me on the merry-go-round in the playground. About all the people I felt had wronged me in some way. Why would I hold on to these things when they did not serve any purpose? Mostly, without getting overly elaborate, they seemed to threaten a deep down sense of security and self. This is why there is so much research about Adverse Childhood Events (ACEs) and trauma and how it relates to addiction. Indeed there are people that believe that these traumatic experiences are directly responsible for all addiction. These things burrow inside and eat away at us. We build a wall of armor so that nothing like that can get to us again, but we don't realize that when we build that wall to keep things out, we also walled in that demon. Things that grow in the dark, die in the light. When I started to share those things, those deep down things, those things we don't talk about, something happened. Something akin to magic. The things that were done to us and the things we have done lose all their power. We can begin looking at how, even the things that weren't our fault, we used those things to fuel the venom we spit at others. I learned that if I was courageous enough to share all those things, I didn't have to hold them anymore. My head is physically able to hold about 1500cubic centimeters of volume. So the biggest problem I can have, the biggest secret I could possibly hold on to, can have no greater volume than that. When I share that secret or problem and I take it out of my head and put it out into the world in the form of word, on paper or tongue, it is still no more than 1500 cubic centimeters in volume. So it was huge in my head, not so much floating around in the world. Sharing that shit magically shrinks it. And sharing it with another person, that takes serious courage. Because what if they think...whatever. I have learned this. People do not think about me nearly as much as I think they do and nothing you ever tell me about you will ever seem as bad to me as my own shit.

**I learned the spiritual principle of humility**

After going through all the shit from my past, there were a few things that were glaringly apparent. I had a lot of fear and resentment. I did not know myself very well. I had *a lot* of shitty characteristics. I was a jealous and insecure person. I was dishonest, manipulative and controlling. I was envious, petty and judgmental. I had a giant ego protecting a terrified spirit. And I hid all of these traits and more, from myself and from everyone else. What I also learned was that I am smart, clever, articulate, insightful (about other people) and confident (in presence). To this day, I still think about conversations with people, like parents of friends, where I cringe to recall how pompous and self righteous I was, hiding behind an air of 'knowledge is power and it is my job to give you the knowledge you clearly don't have.' But this part of my journey required me to really look at these things and become willing to work on them. I had to really be open to the idea that these things, which may have served me well in the past, were no longer helpful. However, before I could be willing to get rid of these things, I had to face it and I was terrified. Because if I was no longer manipulative, dishonest, insecure, egotistical... then who would I be? Would there be anything left? Would whatever was left be worth anything? Would I just be a flat, boring shallow person that was no fun to be around? During one of my rants about this, my friend basically said to me *First of all, you are being pretty fucking dramatic. Second, I don't believe you really fear those things, I think you want to* ***appear*** *to be having a soul struggle about this so that you* ***appear*** *deep and profound. You are more concerned about that than about the actual process. Third, if all that* *is true, and you suck as a human after working on these traits, then you can always take them back and be those shitty things again.* I will never *not* have people like this in my life. People who are honest and hold the mirror up for me. Anyone who knows me will tell you, I pay this forward. Naturally at that time, I became defensive and a little resentful. Then I thought, well, if I take what she just said and I say it at my next therapy session or at a meeting, pretending it was my own conclusion, I will ***appear*** super smart and insightful. Then I thought, well shit, this bitch is right. So I began the work of trying to change.

**I learned the spiritual principle of open mindedness**

Apparently, changing nearly everything about yourself is not as easy as waking up and saying 'today, I will be an honest person.' As it turns out, a lot of these characteristics are, like, seriously rooted in our psyche... or whatever. I can say that I want to no longer manipulate people, but that means nothing if I can't even tell that I am doing it. Or if my dishonest reaction is so nearly instinctual that I can't stop it. My brain is what created these defenses, so how could I count on my brain to identify them in the moment and change them? The answer: I couldn't. I needed to accept that people like the friend above needed to be around me in droves and that I needed to keep my mind open to what they were telling me. I had to be humble enough to know that I would fail at this, probably a lot, before I got better at it. I had to sit down with a bunch of women, some were acquaintances and some friends, all who had gone through this process and tell them all the crappy things about myself and implore them to point out to me if they ever saw these traits pop up for me. I had to tell them that I would probably get defensive at first, but ask them to please keep doing it, even if I respond poorly. So commenced what shall heretofore be known as 'The Very Timely Death of Old Nicole'. Then, day after day, week after week, I had these amazing women telling me if they saw me judging, trying to control, or lying. Over time, very slowly, I began to pause. I learned the art of the pause. The art of 'act don't react.' And if I paused and thought about what I was about to say or do, 99% of the time it was going to be something on my shit list. To avoid the calling out, I would respond differently. I spent so much of my life crafting the 'perfect' image of who I wanted to be: unique, inspirational, confident. But I never actually felt any of these things. Oh, I would wear unusual outfits or do strange things to my hair. I would fill my bookshelves with books I never read but that anyone viewing my bookshelf would interpret as worldly, deep and knowledgeable. I would know just enough about any given subject to speak about it confidently so that I could shut down the conversation before the other person figured out that I didn't know anything. When I started this process of really trying to find out who I was and to be better than I had been, I discovered that what was left was all of those things I had tried to be, but this time authentically, and without trying. A weight was lifted and my own light started to shine through. It was nothing short of miraculous. If I had not believed in a specific higher power up to this point, I started to believe now. I believed that the universe had a magic and an energy that runs through and within all of us. We all have access to it. It shows up for me in the love and support of others. I thank everyone in my journey for allowing my higher power to work through them to keep me clean and growing.

**I learned the spiritual principle of willingness**

Once I had gone through this process of really seeing my bad behaviors showing up over and over and working to change them, it seemed only natural that I would start looking back at a lot of those resentments I had uncovered when I was learning honesty and courage. Little rays of awareness would start seeping through, showing me all the places that my envy and my ego had played a part in all of those things that had happened to me. I started to realize that many of them had happened *because* of me. Fuck. Part of cleaning out my closet involved this discovery, so this was not unexpected, but what was not expected was the desire that I began to have to apologize or make up for some of this stuff. So follow me on this, I initially was like *Mary was a dick to me in high school because she was jealous of me and wanted to turn my friends against me.* But during this process it became more like *Mary was responding to the fact that*

*I was constantly flaunting my achievements and deliberately excluding her from things because I didn't want my friends to like her better.* Now, regardless of whether Mary actually *was* a dick or what her actual intentions were, *I* had my own motives and shitty behavior to be accountable for. So I needed to be willing to find a way to make up for that. Now, please don't misunderstand me on this, this was not an overnight process where I suddenly, in a fit of enlightenment, decided I wanted to apologize to all the Mary's in my life. No, it was more gradual and started with the smaller perceived injustices. As I started the process of 'cleaning up my side of the street,' I realized that it felt good. Sometimes I would send an email to someone after looking them up, like Mary, and just saying 'hey I am sorry for my part.' Sometimes, I could not find someone so I would donate a few bucks to a charity in their name or I would do volunteer hours at a homeless shelter in their honor. As the list of people that I had done something shitty to got smaller and smaller, I felt freer and freer. And the more willing I became to continue.

**I learned the spiritual principle of forgiveness**

One of the people on that list that I had harmed in great amounts, was myself. During this whole process, I got good at congratulating myself for everything that I did well, but I was awfully hard on myself if I fucked up. I always had been. It took going through this process, of saying *ok, old Nicole was a liar and a manipulator and a user and judgmental.* To *Ok, old Nicole needed to be a liar and manipulator and a user and judgmental in order to protect herself from underdeveloped coping skills and any other trauma from childhood. She was not a bad person, she didn't know any better. I forgive her.*

Forgiveness is not about the other person. At all. There were some fucked up things that happened to me in childhood. Maybe in another book I will talk about them, but for our purposes what I need to say is that I have forgiven every single perpetrator. In my heart. I don't hate them. I am neutral toward them. Perhaps someday I will be healed enough to love them. But what I needed to look at is that so many of the shady, manipulative things I have done in my life were done in a figurative fuck you to those people. I hurt other people and myself because deep down I felt like 'well xyz was done to me and I dealt with it, so fuck it, I can do what I want.' This served no one. The person it was subconsciously intended for never even knew, because it had nothing to do with them. But it landed a needle in my arm. In the long run, it also landed me this big ass list of people that I had to apologize to, make amends to, pay back or pay forward.

What I am saying is that for every harm that was done to me, actual or perceived, I had a part in. Either directly at the time or later in carrying the grudge. To extract that poison from my soul I needed to learn to forgive. Forgive them, but mostly forgive me.

**I learned the spiritual principle of gratitude**

This whole process took me the better part of a year to get through. It was a lifetime of shit to dig through, in just under a year. It was like cleaning out a lifetime of hoarding in a basement and when it was done I was viewing the whole space with new eyes and a new goal. Keep it that way. And the only way to do that, in a basement, is to stay on top of it. Every day or once a week, go down and go through whatever had accumulated. The same was true for my spirit. Every day I needed to go through this process, on a smaller scale so that shit didn't pile up again. Every day I have to remember all that I have and how I got it. I have to look at the day and see where I could have improved things, where I am grateful that I did things right. It helps to actually go through this with another person. For the accountability.

I got stuck in a traffic jam driving to work. My first response was to get aggravated. I'd be really frustrated and pissed off because I was going to be late for work, which would put me behind and throw my whole day off. Then I would go home pissy, and my husband and daughter would suffer just because some asshole was speeding or on his phone or whatever and probably killed someone. First, there is nothing I can do about being stuck in traffic. No matter how mad I get, I am still 459 cars behind my exit. I have to accept that I am stuck. Then, I have to acknowledge that being this far behind the accident means that I was not involved in it, that the universe kept me safe, at least for today. I have hope that I will get to work today and will be able to do my job and go home, even if it is a longer more stressful day. Then I have faith that there was a reason for this traffic jam. Perhaps it was to prevent me from being somewhere where *I* could have been in the accident or perhaps it is to cause a change in the way I was going to practice medicine that day. Next, I have to be honest with myself. I could have left a little earlier. I could have taken a different route. I didn't *know* I would get stuck in this, but I still had choices and my choices led me here. I have to be courageous enough to face the day as it is. I have to be humble enough to acknowledge that my immediate response was without compassion. It was entitled and self centered. There are 458 cars also stuck and possibly someone injured or dead up ahead. I make a concerted effort to call someone in my support network and tell on myself for being such a self centered prick and be open to their suggestions as to how I might do this better next time. I have to be willing to do something extra nice for someone later that day to make up for my immediate response of blame. I have to forgive myself for being a douche. I am so incredibly grateful for this process because I have so much less stress, anger and hatred and consequently, my husband and my daughter don't suffer because I have had a bad day. Usually. It's progress not perfection, folks.

**I learned the spiritual principle of discipline**

If I don't practice the piano every day, I will never get to Carnegie Hall. We have already established that I am not a musician. So obviously it is an analogy. I have to practice these things, these spiritual principles, every day. In doing so, I am decreasing the activity in the self centered part of my brain. I am quieting the 'me.' This allows me to focus on overcoming the desire to escape, to feel different, to be comfortably numb. When I don't practice, however, all the defaults start showing up. Old Nicole comes knocking at the door and she is smart and clever and subtle. It's not like if I don't go through this process daily for a few weeks that I suddenly wake up and start lying to everyone. No, it starts out with one little white lie or one subtle manipulation. Maybe of my husband, maybe a coworker. Then I find myself in a strange, but comfortable place of feeling guilty, but trying to justify or rationalize what I did. Then I can either tell on myself or continue to cover up and maintain the lie until I am in such a stressed out state that I blow up.

**I learned the spiritual principle of service**

The easiest way to continue to practice these principles is to teach others to do the same. I work in a field where I have the potential to be helpful to others, and I am grateful for that. Not everyone does and not everyone has time to volunteer at the dog shelter or work in a food bank. But being of service and helping others is the best way to maintain the quietude of that right parietal lobe. So teach. Share what you learned in your journey. It doesn't matter if the person you are sharing with actually follows your advice or example. It only matters that you offered it.

TWENTY - FOUR

# DON'T SETTLE FOR SURVIVE...*THRIVE*

*"You yourself as much as anybody in the entire universe, deserve your love and affection."*

– Gautama Buddha

I have proposed throughout this book that addiction is a disease. A chronic disease. However, it seems that most works about addiction focus on a few different concepts: the memoir of the individual, the actual disease or whatever it is being touted as, and treatments for the immediate disease state. Basically, we tend to focus on how not to die. We talk about putting down the drug and we talk about learning some skills so we don't pick up again. We talk about looking at our past and digging deep to figure out why we started using in the first place. There are lots of books talking about the best types of groups to run, the best psychotherapy skills to introduce, and the best ways to detox. But a chronic disease is that, chronic. It is the reason that I know from my own experience that if I do not continue to practice the things that got me clean, the old patterns of thought and behavior resurface. I am not the only one. I have seen it first hand in the rooms of twelve step groups, and I have seen it in my patients. Same story, different faces.

So, yes, those skills need to be continually practiced and utilized. That is enough to prevent relapse, for most people. But my question is why is this enough? No addict ever asked to be an addict. Most of them had dreams, hopes and aspirations. Most still do. So much effort is being exerted on teaching addicts how to stay clean and not die, that life after not dying seems to get forgotten. I mean, it would seem that if this is a disease, and diseases rarely affect only one body system, then treating the whole person makes sense. Why aren't we doing this? Addicts beat the shit out of their bodies while they are using, then they stop using drugs and alcohol but continue to put garbage into it, in the form of processed foods, sugar and energy drinks. They continue to smoke cigarettes and binge watch television or play video games. They continue to just 'exist' as a parent, a spouse, a child and while they take some pride (as they should) in being a 'clean and sober' parent, spouse and/or child, we aren't offering them anymore than that. Part of treating the chronic disease that affects the mind, body and spirit should really include continuous and lifelong development of mind, body and spirit. In general, I think that if any person wants to become well, they need to take care of all aspects of themselves. Addicts have the distinct advantage of already doing a lot of work on themselves, so they need only apply the same discipline to these other areas of their lives to really benefit from the continuous wealth of health. Plus, continuously developing and focusing on physical mental and spiritual well-being will make it that much easier to avoid falling back into the world of using.

There are literally hundreds of thousands of resources, books, blogs, magazines, documentaries, that focus on personal development. Any of them could be useful, but I know that when faced with a hundred thousand choices, I become paralyzed. It has taken nearly fourteen years of recovery to really find a groove and a structure that works for me. I have read thousands of books on nutrition, diets and nutrients. I have done every kind of exercise class I could find. I have a home gym full of videos, games, equipment, and inspirational wall quotes. I have watched hundreds of documentaries on spirituality, meaning and purpose in life. I would take bits and pieces here and there and try to apply them, but I was never good at applying a little bit of change into each area of my life. Maybe because I am an addict, I crave novelty, so I easily fall victim to thirty and ninety day programs to 'change my life.' What I don't crave is daily grind. Nor daily practice. Yet this is the only thing that has consistently worked for me.

I would love to apply what I have learned to the wellness of my patients and I am working on how to do that. Unfortunately, most treatment facilities have to be able to keep the lights on and to pay the people that are working on the 'teaching people how to not die' part of things. So it is really difficult to treat the continuum of this disease. How do I teach the various stages of adequate nutrition to improve ALL areas of health when my schedule is full of people I am trying to keep alive and no insurance will pay for this aspect of treatment. I know there are some fancy treatment centers that do this, but I am pretty sure they are limited to the wealthy. Most of my patients are coming off the streets and barely have their necessities taken care of, so that seems like a priority. Asking them to sacrifice their rent or car payment to pay for a yoga course seems elitist. The truth is, most addicts and addict family members want nothing more than to read a book about how getting IV vitamins for five days in a center will be the answer to their prayers. Not only is it hard to get the information out in a practical way, but it is hard to motivate people that still find instant gratification more appealing than actual work.

So how do we get this knowledge, coupled with some structure, into the hands of addicts to practice?

The following are very basic tips and ideas for growth and improvement beyond just not using. If you want something solid to sink your teeth into... well... at least put your pen to, there is a workbook, written by myself and my much smarter colleague, Cherie Shanko, MSW, LISW[38] and it is available on Amazon. It is called *The Addiction Workbook: a Companion Guide for Substance Abuse Treatment.* It contains quick and easy exercises to supplement recovery. Throughout this section, where applicable, I will refer to a specific exercise in that workbook (if you are a workbook type of person.) The link for the workbook can be found on my website at www.theaddictsdoc.com.

---

38 When I say the workbook was written by both of us, what I mean is that I had an abstract, nebulous idea of what I wanted to create and Cherie was able to actually create a concrete and much better version of those ideas. Which is why she gets top billing on that book.

**1.Eat proper nutrition.**

If taking a blood pressure medication, a single pill, can change the entire cardiovascular system for 24 hours, then why would we think that a chemical that we ingest multiple times throughout a day would not have significant effects on our bodies? Food is a chemical. At least, structurally speaking. All foods, even the natural ones grown in the earth, are made up of chemical structures and these chemical structures impact our health. For better or worse. What we choose to put into our bodies matters. It really does. If we are trying to prevent anxiety, pain, boredom, fatigue... all potential triggers for relapse, then why would we not consider nutrition to be paramount? Water alone has the ability to decrease anxiety, pain, and fatigue in addition to a number of other benefits. What you eat will work to keep you depressed, tired and irritable or it will promote a sense of well being, energy and health. Guess which is more likely to lead to relapse. Eat more vegetables. Eat more mindfully. Also, drink water. Not sweetened water, just water. Put fruit in it. Get the carbonated kind. But for fuck's sake, please drink water.
*(workbook exercise title: Eat Proper Nutrition)*

**2. Move More.**

You don't have to train for marathons or fitness competitions, but you need to move more than what is required to go from point A to point B in as few steps as possible. Our bodies are not designed to be sedentary. We sit too much or get stuck in the same repetitive motion. Over time this causes our bones to weaken, our muscles to atrophy, our joints to stiffen and our skin to sag. (Ok, maybe not that last one.) Non exercise activity thermogenesis (NEAT) is just our normal movement. If we want to benefit from movement, we need to go above and beyond our 'normal.' I often hear from people that work physically demanding jobs that they don't 'need' to exercise because they are 'on my feet all day' or 'lifting fifty pound boxes all day' at work. Unfortunately for them, the body adapts. Those activities are no longer benefiting them beyond keeping them from being totally sedentary. If I were to spend the day lifting fifty pound boxes, it would be both cardiovascular and strength training. If it is your job, then your exercise needs to include stuff outside of that. Sorry.

What is right for you? I don't know. Maybe you do want to train for marathons or build crazy huge muscles. Seriously, that's cool, but not necessary. It all just comes down to making movement a part of your life. So jumping on the bandwagon of doing an hour workout every day for ninety days will likely be having you feeling good (did I mention exercise releases endorphins? These are our natural opioids), it will not be sustainable once the novelty wears off unless you absolutely love the activity you are doing. Anyone can pencil in a workout for ninety days, it is the 'end in sight' that allows us to prioritize it. That may not be realistic for many people and addicts in particular are quick to say, "Fuck it. I can't do forty five minutes a day between my job and family. So I won't do anything."

Start small, like really small, such as a five or ten minute walk everyday. Like the kind of small that you don't need to consult your doctor before starting. You don't necessarily need to do it the same time every day, but somewhere in the day. Make it non-negotiable. Don't be like me and spend years telling yourself that a ten minute walk isn't going to do anything so why bother, as I sit on the couch and search my phone for ways to lose weight and gain energy. Just move more.

*(workbook exercise title: Move More)*

**3. Get connected.**

There is a series of experiments done in the 1970s by psychologist Bruce K. Alexander and his colleagues at Simon Fraser University in Canada that basically took a bunch of rats, similar to the Olds experiments mentioned earlier, and offered them drug laced water vs. plain water. Consistent with the earlier experiments, the rats that were kept alone in a cage preferred the drug. However, rats that were allowed to run free in a 'rat park' with a bunch of other rats, actually preferred the plain water. In 1939, a book was published about how a group of alcoholics could sustainably help other alcoholics stay sober through fellowship with one another and shared experience. This book is now known as The Big Book of Alcoholics Anonymous. More than thirty years before testing the theory on rats, humans had shown that connectedness and socialization was a key factor in recovering from addiction.

When I was training in addiction medicine, I had a physician tell me that addicts just need to find purpose and they could do that through gainful employment. I struggled with this, because many of my patients had been gainfully employed when they started using substances. So, for some, those who have truly found their calling, their job or career might provide them with some purpose. But for others, I just don't see how. Certainly having work can help a person with self esteem and provide some sense of security, and these things are important, but by themselves are likely to be ineffective for the long haul.

Most addicts are uncomfortable with other people, have trust issues, or just feel awkward. So they cling to the support people that have been around for the longest like old friends that don't use or family members. Then they are confused and frustrated when they relapse over and over. Now, I won't pretend to understand the neuroscience behind the different types of relationships with people, but I do know that I see the most success in treating addiction in two scenarios:

(1) The addict steps out of their comfort zone and develops new relationships with people who understand what they are going through.

(2)The addict finds a way to help others. This goes back to that spiritual part of the brain, the decreasing of the 'me- centeredness' and the increasing of the 'other-centeredness'.

Many addicts find their purpose here. Their growth in self love and self worth becomes exponential and they truly Thrive.
*(workbook exercise title: Social Support Network)*

**4. Get to know yourself.**

So many of us lose ourselves in our addictions. When we emerge, we are left with this sense of 'who am I?' Once we learn how to set boundaries, identify triggers, and utilize all of the skills we learn in treatment, it is time to start really trying to figure ourselves out.

The frontal cortex is the "home base." This is where the brain assigns emotional meaning to things in the world and allows personality to develop. It is especially important for how someone sees themselves, manages behavior, and makes rational decisions. Some functions of the frontal cortex include learning, memory, attention, and motivation. The frontal cortex is also responsible for a person's set of values and personality. While someone's values and personality may be somewhat 'set', we still need to develop a picture of what those look like.

This may seem daunting, but it is really quite simple if you do it one bite sized piece at a time. Start by identifying your likes and dislikes. Don't assume that the story you have been telling yourself for your entire life is true. You may actually like brussel sprouts (when they are crispy fried with bacon and cheese) or you may find that you are able to admit (to yourself at least) that you actually enjoy listening to Nickelback. Keep a journal and try things that you have never tried before and re-try things that you think you like and don't like. I am not talking about a 'bucket list', although that may be something you want to pursue in recovery. No, I am not advocating for a sudden interest in sky diving and bungee jumping when those things weren't on your radar. I am simply suggesting that you try some things that you never had time for in addiction. Pottery, painting, gardening, bowling...whatever piques your interest. Develop a list of your strengths and assets. Spend some time learning about social and political issues that interest you or develop some new daily habits. So if you were to introduce yourself to someone, what would you say?

I spent a summer going to a ton of shows by the band Phish. If you would have asked me, even after I got out of rehab, if I enjoyed going to concerts, I would have scoffed at the question. As it turns out, I don't like going to concerts. I liked drinking and getting high at concerts, I liked hanging out with a bunch of other people drinking and getting high. But, I am just as content to listen to my favorite bands hanging out on my couch. And, it turns out that I don't even like Phish that much.

I had no idea who I was and there is a good chance if you are in early recovery, that you don't either. But the good news is that starting with a clean slate is actually kind of fun. You might realize that you are a ninja warrior pirate superhero. Maybe that's just me. *(workbook exercise title: Functions of the frontal cortex)*

**5. Learn to prioritize.**

One of the areas that I struggled with the most was learning to prioritize. It seemed like a no brainer that paying my bills and maintaining my relationships with my family should be #1 on my list. However, after a thorough evaluation of my values, I was able to determine that my recovery needed to come first, because if I let that slip, I would lose all the rest. Next on the list, though, was myself. Self care. We undervalue this so much. When we talk about self care, we associate it with things like getting a massage and taking a bubble bath. Those things can be self care, but it is really more about setting up our lives to have the least amount of stress. We can't avoid stress, but we also can't avoid responsibilities. So making it a daily habit to take care of our responsibilities, even the annoying ones (like doing the dishes), are a form of self care. If you are anything like me, and you probably are, you have let things slide. Until you wake up one day and are cranky and irritable and there are just so many things on the to do list because you let them build up. This could be household chores or it could be paying your bills on time.

When the airplane is going down and the masks pop out, you have to put yours on first or you will pass out before you can help your kids or spouse or anyone else with theirs. Taking the time and setting up structure and priorities based on our values allows us to avoid unnecessary stress and then we actually find that we have time (and maybe some money) to enjoy that massage or bubble bath.
If that's your thing. *(workbook exercise title: values)*

**6. Set goals.**

In early (and even later) recovery, we start to see a light at the end of the tunnel. We are coming out of the darkness into a bright new world. We are suddenly flooded with all these ideas and things we want to do and accomplish. Time after time I see my patients just going through the daily grind with big dreams and no action. And isn't because they aren't motivated or don't have the ability to achieve those goals, but because they have no idea how to achieve them. The acronym SMART stands for Specific, Measurable, Achievable, Relevant and Time Bound. A SMART goal is a defined stepping stone that a person takes towards what they want to accomplish as a long-term goal. Having goals written in a SMART format defines what is trying to be accomplished, why it is important, when it will be completed, and how it will be achieved.

I hear people say all the time "I should write a book" but less than 4% of all people actually write a book. I have been sitting on the idea of a book for a long time, but it wasn't until I made it a goal, that I started to work toward it in any type of productive way.

*Specific:* I want to write a book about addiction and include pieces of my story.

*Measurable*: you are holding/reading this book right now, so it was measurable by being a completed project.

*Achievable*: obviously I was able to achieve it, but I needed to break down the how. I said I would sit down and write for two hours each night after my kid went to sleep until I finished. I would forgo *America's Got Talent* and *Murder, She Wrote* re-runs until the project was complete. I would enlist the help of other self published authors for direction in areas that I didn't know about or understand (like editing, formatting and marketing).

*Relevant*: I do a lot of educating, both one-on-one with patients as well as the community. It seemed to me like people were thirsty for information about addiction in a way that they could understand and relate.

*Time Bound*: I set a date for each stage of the process and worked each day to, more or less, hit those goals.
*(workbook exercise title(s): SMART Goals, My SMART Goal)*

**7. Learn to save.**

Ugh. I am the worst at this. It has taken me years to learn the skill of saving money. But saving doesn't have to be limited to finances. When people first get into recovery we advise that they 'stockpile' recovery. That is, we advise getting as much counseling, skills and social support as they possibly can cram into a day. Because someday, Recovery will give you a life again, but you don't want that life to take away your recovery. Developing new habits and social networks is hard and uncomfortable. Guess when that is the hardest to do? When you are comfortable. So if you spend all your time in early recovery focusing on rebuilding your relationships with your family or working a million hours to catch up on your bills, you aren't saving any recovery because you are barely getting enough to keep you clean day to day. But if you are practicing calling sober supports and spending time each day developing a meditation practice, then when shit hits the fan eight months down the road, you already have a 'savings account' of recovery skills.

The same needs to be said for securing a financial future. Look, I am a doctor. And, while I have an inordinate amount of student loan debt and other self inflicted debt, I am comfortable. I am not naive enough to believe that in today's economy that everyone else will be as fortunate as I am. But the skill of saving matters far more than the amount. Because over time, it matters. Even a little matters. If you can have even 10% of your paycheck automatically deposited somewhere that you can't see it or get to it easily, you are far less likely to spend it and unlikely to notice it missing at all. Even if you live paycheck to paycheck. I am by no means a financial expert, but I do have goals and dreams for the future. And, if I did not take the steps to save some dollars, my Amazon shopping endeavors would ensure that I would be working until I died with nothing to show for it.

Even just the act of putting one dollar a week in a jar or piggy bank that you have sealed shut will reap the rewards...not just of saved cash, but a sense of accomplishment.

Save moments. Don't spend so much time thinking about what you still have to do that day, month or year, enjoy the moments you have with your loved ones. We spend so much time trying to

get to a magical place that we have created in our minds where we will be 'good' and able to just relax and enjoy our family and friends that we miss all the opportunities to be with them, both in mind and body, right now. Save those precious minutes, hours and days. Because no one ever winds up on their deathbed saying, "I wish I hadn't spent so much time with my loved ones."
*(workbook exercise title(s): Stockpile Recovery/Save Moments/Build Your Savings)*

**8. Learn mindfulness.**

As far as I am concerned, if you take nothing else away from this experience with me, learn mindfulness. It is the most rewarding and powerful skill I have ever encountered and is the foundation for so many of the other skills I have discussed. Most simply, mindfulness is the practice of being fully present in the moment. There is a saying that if you have one foot in the future and one in the past, you are pissing on today. We spend so much time anticipating, worrying about and having expectations for the future. No wonder we are all so anxious. If we aren't dwelling on some not-yet-existent-and-probably-never-will-be future, we are fixated on the past. Feeling guilty, stupid, regretful and remorseful. About shit that we can't do anything about anymore (aside from the amends we have already made). How many times have you laid in bed and rehashed a conversation you had earlier in the day or week? Re-creating entire discussions and beating yourself up over what you wish you would have said or done? Waste. Of. Fucking. Time. But we do it all the time.

Stop. Stop reading (right after this paragraph) and quiet your mind for ten seconds and just notice this very moment. Notice your breathing, notice the feeling of the book pressed against your hands. Notice any smells or sounds. Don't interpret them (mmm that smells like banana bread. No. Just 'I smell something' or 'I hear a noise'). Notice that in this very moment in time, no matter what is happening in your life, everything is ok. Just this second. And then repeat. Do it enough times and life becomes very calm and serene and nothing is as bad as you thought.

When I first learned mindfulness, I was told to eat an almond. One almond. Hold it in my hand and notice what it feels like. The texture, the hardness, the shape. Look at it, and notice the same things. Smell it. Taste it. Roll in around in my mouth and feel the texture and shape of it. Does the taste change if it is in my mouth for a while? Do I notice an increase in salivation? Chew it. Slowly. Stopping to notice if the texture and tastes change as I chew it. And so on. I learned three things during this process. I learned that I rarely pay attention to things right in front of me. I learned that this process took me out of all of my chaotic thinking. I learned that doing this with ten almonds one at a time was enough to make me feel full. Just ten. How many times had I thrown handful after handful of nuts into my piehole, mindlessly, just chomping away, not even noticing them? Too many, my friends, too many.

This skill takes practice though. The mind wants to race on to the next thing and the next thing and the next. Learning to rein it in and pay attention is hard. But so so rewarding.

*(workbook exercise title(s): Mindful Meditation/Your Happy Place)*

## FREQUENTLY ASKED QUESTIONS

There are a number of questions that come up often that just did not lend themselves to the flow of this book, however, I did not want to neglect them.

1. **As a family member, what is the best way for me to help my loved one who is an addict?**

Ok, so this question is actually usually asked as, "how can I make my loved one stop using?" and the answer is, you can't. No one can make an addict stop using until they are ready and there is no way to know what is going to make someone ready. People like to speculate. Even doctors will say things like, "He is in complete liver failure and needs a transplant. I think it's safe to say that this is his bottom," (I swear on my dog that a doctor actually said this). But no, that is not how it works. We do not get to decide when enough is enough for someone else. For some, the loss of relationships is what it takes. For others, the loss of a job or financial security. Some people have a 'spiritual' bottom, where they just can't take feeling so lost and alone and 'sick and tired of being sick and tired.' There is talk of low bottoms and high bottoms. A low bottom would be one where someone has suffered enormous loss and consequence due to their use. They may be homeless, have legal issues, be unemployed and have been ostracized by their families. They may have serious medical complications.

A high bottom would be where they have not necessarily lost anything, yet, but they know they are on the verge of losing things. Sometimes, people get into recovery with a high bottom, relapse, and don't make it back into treatment until they reach a very low bottom.

The truth is that there is no such thing as an actual 'bottom.' It is simply the point at which an addict comes to the conclusion that they are ready to change and worth the effort. If this happens early on in their use, great. If it happens later, great. The hope is simply that it happens before their disease kills them.

As a family member, you can't make them look at their current situation and decide they are done. Trust me, they *know* how bad things are. They are using every damn day to escape the reality of how bad things are.

What you *can* do, however, is set a good example. Stop being an actor in the drama and start setting boundaries for yourself. Decide what you will and will not tolerate, and to what degree you will extract yourself from the situation. Remember, you can only control your emotions, your feelings and your actions. Not theirs. So take responsibility for that. If you are tired of sleeping with the car keys in the pillowcase, stop doing that. Don't allow someone who would steal your car keys to be entering your house. If you don't like that your addict is spending all their rent money on drugs, don't give them extra money to make up for it. If life as a using addict isn't all that difficult, there is little reason to stop using.

I am a parent. I thoroughly understand the paralyzing fear at the thought of losing your child. However, there is no difference between a child that overdoses in a trap house with the money they stole from someone, and a child that overdoses in your basement with the money you gave them. They are both dead. Perhaps an individual that has to sleep on the streets for a few weeks, though, may decide that this life is too hard and decide to reach out for help.

The twelve step programs for family members, family counseling and individual counseling are great resources. They will not, however, tell you how to fix your addict. They will tell you how to fix yourself. If you are focusing on your addict the way that they focus on drugs, they are your drug of choice and you have the same problem that they do.

So set a good example by learning about boundaries, about loving detachment, and about staying in your hula hoop.[39] This will only serve you well. If your addict gets well, then great, you can continue to grow together. If your addict does not get well, you are getting to a place where you will be emotionally strong enough to deal with that. The harsh reality is that addiction is a disease that kills people. Your addict may die before they get well and if you don't have the appropriate coping skills, you may just honor their life with your own downward spiral.

39 Take a hula hoop and place it on the floor. Step into the center of it. Everything inside the hula hoop is yours. It is your responsibility and your business. Everything outside the hula hoop is none of your business and a waste of time, energy and resources for you to try to fix or change it.

**2. What about pain? Some addicts have real pain. Can they take opioids?**

Addicts do have real pain. Unfortunately, for the most part, once addiction occurs, addicts no longer have the privilege of chemical comfort. Not because we want them to suffer but because the risk of relapse is so high. In some rare circumstances, there is no choice but for an addict to take a prescribed, addictive substance. There are safeguards that could be put in place but, they are tedious and inconvenient for everyone involved. Aside from those rare cases, here is what I want people to know and understand. Pain is not a bad thing. Pain tells us that our body is hurt, or damaged. It tells us that we may need to stop doing something to give it time to heal. Also, freedom from pain is not a right. Pain management was never meant to get people to a place of being pain free. It was meant to take someone who could not function in life, because of pain, to a place of functioning.

If your job is building houses and that job caused you to develop arthritis in your back and perhaps you herniated a disk, pain management is not meant to mask that pain so you can continue doing the same damage. "But I'm a builder and that is how I support my family so I can't quit." Ok, but then you will keep causing damage, keep taking and needing more pain meds until it gets out of control again. Then eventually you will spend all your money on heroin and lose your job/business. Now, tell me again how you need to support your family. This is like hitting your hand with a hammer over and over and then demanding something for the pain while you continue to hit it.

Many painful conditions actually do resolve themselves with time and/or work. Physical therapy was designed to strengthen the muscles around the injured area so that it is better supported and less likely to be reinjured. But here we are again,talking about actual work, talking about how it will take time to get better. There is something even more nefarious going on that no one tells you about. Opiates make pain worse. Read that again.

Now I will attempt to explain (this is so much easier if I have pictures). You have a site of injury, say a bulging disk in the lower back. When there is an injury/pain, the body sends a bunch of stuff out to the site like first responders. These are things like histamines and prostaglandins and iterleukins. These things get to work quickly setting up an emergency shelter. They perform tasks like cause inflammation around the injury because inflammation is fluid and fluid cushions the area. They set up some muscle spasms because the muscle needs to hold the spine still until they get to the bottom of what is going on. And they send out the pain signal like a bat signal to the brain saying "SOMETHING IS WRONG HERE. SOMETHING IS NOT RIGHT, PAIN, PAIN... ALERT THE OTHERS." This signal is sent via nerve cells/pathways. There are several different paths that are used just in case any of them get stuck in traffic. Each of these paths is moderated by a different class of drug. So there is a pathway that is mainly a nerve pathway. It tells the brain that there may be nerves damaged. It can be blocked by medications like gabapentin and Lyrica. There are inflammatory pathways, which tells the brain there is inflammation. It is blocked by anti-inflammatories. There are pathways that are blocked by certain antidepressants and there is a big fat fiber optic cable pathway for opiates. This is by far the strongest path. So when it is blocked, by opiates, it creates the most relief. The problem here is that when this signal is blocked by opiates, the brain starts to wonder what the hell is going on down there in the low back. It isn't getting any new information and it assumes the disk is still bulging. So it sends out road crews to start constructing new opiate pathways. Now, the person thinks the pain seems to be getting worse, because there are new pain signals and the opiates they have been taking are no longer helping as much. So they need more. The additional opiates block the new pathways and then even more new ones are formed. This keeps going on and on.

Then, they get cut off of the opiates. Either they just decide to stop or they are unable to get any. So they go through opiate withdrawal which amplifies ALL pain, so during that period everything seems worse. But after the withdrawal, the person is left with all these new opiate pain pathways plus the original big fat pathway. *Even if the disk is no longer injured/bulging.*

If they remain off the opiates entirely for a period of time, usually about six months, the new pathways die off and the original pathway starts to shrink down to a signal commensurate with what is actually going on at the injury site. Those other, non-opiate pathways can be used to help a little during this time, but for the most part, this person is going to have pain most likely out of proportion for several months. One day, they will suddenly find that it is tolerable, if not better. Accepting that they may have some bad days going forward where they may need to just rest is part of treating the disease of chronic pain. Then they need to focus on working on their core strength to shore up the spine and protect it from another injury.

Going to a chronic pain support group can also help. Relating to others who suffer in a similar way can be therapeutic as well as provide tips and tricks for reducing pain and discomfort without the use of addictive substances.

Only you can decide if the pain is really bad enough to warrant the risk of falling back into active addiction. The reality is that that is most likely what will happen and there is no getting around that. Did I mention somewhere that life is not fair? It isn't.

### 3. What about mental illness? Is addiction just a result of self medicating depression or anxiety?

Mental illness is complex, but there are a couple of points that I like people to understand. To begin, the kind of depression that people suffer from in mental illness is generally a serotonin and a norepinepherine problem in areas other than the reward center. The symptoms of this would likely have been present prior to ever using a substance if this is the primary problem. If depression was diagnosed within a year of the last use of a substance, however, it is entirely possible that it is the dopamine dysthymia (or substance induced depressive disorder). People really like to jump on the bandwagon of feeling like their use was justified because they are depressed. I am not saying someone could not have developed one of these organic depressions during their use, but I am saying that even if the anti-depressants are helping during active use and/or early recovery, they may work differently once the dopamine system is restored because the extra serotonin or norepinepherine may have been compensating for the lack of dopamine. So when the dopamine comes back, the other neurotransmitters may be too abundant, or at least disproportionate to need. Treatment for mental illness needs to be monitored very closely during the first year of recovery and adjustments to medications made as soon as possible. Preferably by a psychiatrist that actually understands addiction.

Also, anxiety works in a similar way, except some of the meds for anxiety are super addictive themselves. So whenever possible with an addict, anxiety should be treated with non-benzoanxiolytics (antianxiety meds) or, preferably, cognitive behavioral therapy.

Mood disorders like Bipolar are not likely being helped all that much by illicit drugs, and in fact, the highs and lows of Bipolar disorder could be exacerbated by certain substances.

The fact of the matter is such that even if the addict is self medicating mental illness, they have developed the disease of addiction. So treating the mental illness will not treat the addiction. It will certainly aid the recovery process to have the rest of the brain chemistry ship shape, but it won't treat the addiction.

Much of the treatment for mental illness includes the cognitive skills sets learned in treatment for addiction. If someone has both mental illness and addiction, the addiction must be addressed first (unless the person is suicidal, in which case that needs to be addressed immediately). This is because it becomes very difficult to get the medications correctly adjusted if the person is consistently fucking with the brain chemistry by adding foreign chemicals (ie drugs and alcohol) to the mix.

Trauma is different and we addressed that earlier.

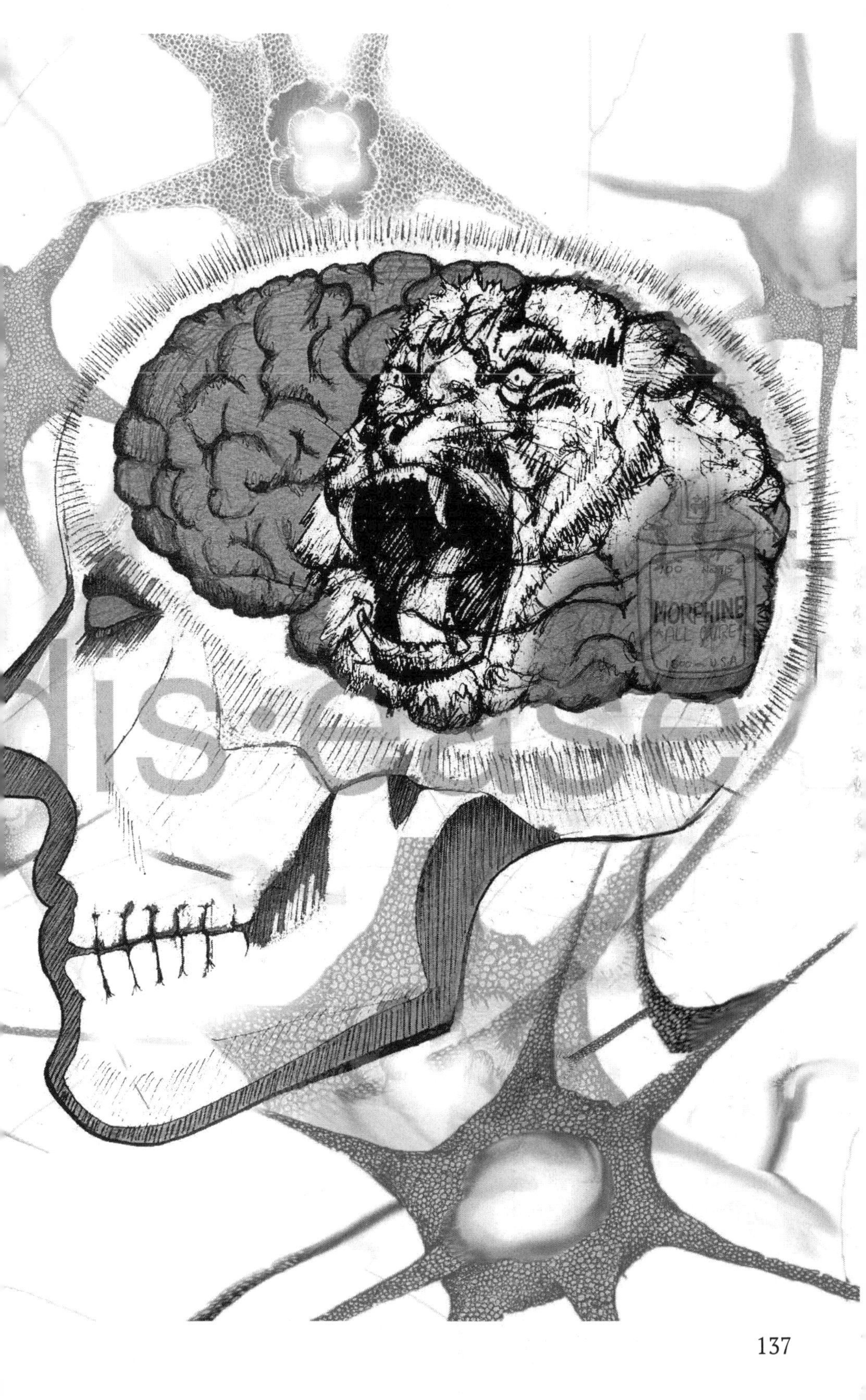
disease
MORPHINE
ALL CURE

# SUMMARY

I hope this book was helpful to you. If not, I hope you got it from Amazon because they will take that shit back and give you a refund. If you got it somewhere else, sorry, you're probably beat. For those that enjoyed it, I know that was a lot of information so, let's recap. The moral of the story is that addiction is a disease. There are genetic and biological components of it that are undeniable and that qualify it as a disease, like all the other diseases. There is an organ (the brain). There is a defect in the organ, the decrease in dopamine receptors, the decrease in cortical skill sets and the increase in the 'me' centered part of the brain (or a defect in spirituality). There are symptoms including: craving, continued use despite negative consequences, violation of one's value systems, inability to experience delayed gratification, inability to just stop and loss of control/acting like a fool. Left untreated, addiction will always result in death. Addiction is chronic, but treatable. And, just like other chronic diseases, lifelong maintenance is needed to prevent relapse. The cessation of use is necessary to survival, but the development of coping skills and social supports as well as finding purpose in life are necessary to thrive. Learn self care. Learn to forgive yourself and others. Learn to know and love yourself.

And above all, drink water.

## PAGE OF SHIT THAT NOBODY CARES ABOUT

Except Editors And Maybe Some Academics,
AKA: Works Cited

It has been about 2000 years since I was in any kind of academic situation where I had to properly cite my work. I have no recollection of proper formatting and am not going to relearn it.

I have mentioned several books and their authors, they're mentioned in the actual text and/or footnotes, I am not repeating them here.

I referred to a few government agencies that have websites you can look at, check the footnotes.

I cited an article, also in the footnotes.

All of the quotes used are either in the public domain or I have obtained permission prior to publication.

That's the best you are going to get. Again, I accept full responsibilty for the fact that this level of laziness makes me a shittier author.

Have a nice day.

# ACKNOWLEDGEMENTS

I want to thank Cherie Shanko for being my beta reader, general sounding board and all around friend throughout this project.

My cousin Kevin who found the time to help me with the artistic side of things despite his many many many roles.

I want to thank my patients and community members who have supported and encouraged me throughout my career and given me the confidence and inspiration to write this book.

I want to thank Margaret Jarvis, MD and David J. Withers, MD for mentoring me, encouraging me and believing in me.

I want to thank Kevin McCauley, MD for his work on Pleasure Unwoven, hands down the biggest inspiration and greatest source of cleverness for this book.

## ABOUT the AUTHOR

Dr. Labor graduated from the Pennsylvania State University with a Bachelor's of Science degree in BioBehavioral Health. She attended and graduated medical school in Erie Pennsylvania at the Lake Erie College of Osteopathic Medicine. She completed a residency in Family Practice at the State University of New York in Buffalo, New York period followed by a fellowship in addiction medicine through Geisinger in northeastern Pennsylvania. She is currently the medical director at OneEighty, a treatment center that offers inpatient and outpatient chemical dependency and behavioral health services in Wooster, OH. She is also the director of the addiction medicine Fellowship for Summa. Dr. Labor is also medical director for Interval Brotherhood Home, a residential treatment facility in Akron, OH as well as the Esper Treatment Center in Erie, PA.

Dr. Labor spends time educating healthcare professionals, churches, schools and community members on the disease of addiction and works to remove the stigma surrounding addiction. Many of her lectures have been unofficially recorded and are available on social media.

She lives with her husband and daughter on a small hobby farm in Seville, OH. You can contact Dr. Labor through her website: www.theaddictsdoc.com

Made in the USA
Columbia, SC
23 February 2021